Essential Mathematics for Chemists

We work with leading authors to develop the
strongest educational materials in mathematics,
bringing cutting-edge thinking and best learning
practice to a global market.

Under a range of well-known imprints, including
Prentice Hall, we craft high quality print and
electronic publications which help readers to
understand and apply their content,
whether studying or at work.

To find out more about the complete range of our
publishing please visit us on the World Wide Web at:
www.pearsoneduc.com

Essential Mathematics for Chemists

JOHN GORMALLY

An imprint of **Pearson Education**

Harlow, England · London · New York · Reading, Massachusetts · San Francisco · Toronto · Don Mills, Ontario · Sydney
Tokyo · Singapore · Hong Kong · Seoul · Taipei · Cape Town · Madrid · Mexico City · Amsterdam · Munich · Paris · Milan

Pearson Education Limited
Edinburgh Gate
Harlow
Essex CM20 2JE
England

and Associated Companies throughout the world

Visit us on the World Wide Web at:
www.pearsoneduc.com

First edition 2000

© Pearson Education Limited 2000

ISBN 0130-86345-9

British Library Cataloguing-in-Publication Data
A catalogue record for this book can be obtained from the British Library

Library of Congress Cataloging-in-Publication Data
Gormally, J. (John)
    Essential mathematics for chemists / John Gormally.–1st ed.
      p. cm.
    Includes bibliographical references and index.
    ISBN 0-13-086345-9
    1. Chemistry–Mathematics. I. Title.

QD42.G63 2000
$540'.'51-dc21$ 99-088911

10 9 8 7 6 5 4 3 2 1
04 03 02 01 00

Typeset by 60 in $10/12\frac{1}{2}$ pt Times
Printed by Ashford Colour Press Ltd., Gosport

Contents

7   Matrix algebra   136

Index   147

Preface

This book is intended for students who are studying chemistry and chemistry related subjects on degree and other higher level courses. Such courses invariably have some mathematical content, but the mathematical background of students studying on them can be very varied. For this reason, the book has been written so that those without extensive prior mathematical knowledge will be able to progress through it at a level that is suited to their needs. This treatment of the subject derives from a course given by the author at the University of Salford over a number of years.

Chapters have been written in an order that reflects the way in which courses in chemistry are often structured, but the order in which they are studied could be adapted to suit the needs of individual students. Chapters 1 and 3 deal with material that may be encountered in laboratory work. Chapters 2 and 4 are concerned with functions that arise in the study of chemistry and with elementary algebraic manipulation. Students who wish to defer the study of laboratory related material could start by reading the section on logarithmic and exponential functions in Chapter 2 before moving on to Chapter 4. The material in these four chapters should be regarded as core mathematics that all students of chemistry need to become familiar with in the early stages of their course. Chapters 5 and 6 deal with differential and integral calculus and have been written with the needs of those who have no prior knowledge of calculus in mind. Chapter 7 is an introduction to matrix algebra. A knowledge of this topic is not required for all chemistry courses but students on courses that do require such a knowledge will find it advantageous to have met with the topic before being confronted with it in a physical chemistry text.

All chapters contain self test questions at various points in the text and it is strongly recommended that students attempt these questions as they occur. Answers to self test questions are given at the end of each chapter. In addition, other longer problems will be found at the end of each chapter. These are intended as exercises that may be set by tutors.

Students of chemistry are often understandably anxious that any mathematics that they study should be relevant to their needs. However, a word of caution should be issued regarding the question of relevance. If students hope to become both competent and confident in their use of mathematics, they cannot afford to restrict their study only to those problems that are directly relevant to chemistry, as the range and number of such problems is not sufficient to allow for adequate practice. Some of the problems presented in this book have little direct relevance to chemistry but it is important that students attempt them in order that they will feel confident in their approach to those problems that are relevant to their subject.

John Gormally

1 Handling numbers

The most commonly used method of representing numbers derives from the set of negative and positive **integers**, or whole numbers, including 0:

$$\ldots -5, -4, -3, -2, -1, 0, 1, 2, 3, 4, 5 \ldots$$

Not all numbers are members of this set. However, most numbers that are not in this set can be represented using symbols from it. For example, a number midway between 2 and 3 could be written as $2\frac{1}{2}$ or, in decimal notation, as 2.5.

1.1 Decimal representation

In decimal representation, a number is written in the format

number = sign integer.tenths hundredths thousandths . . .

for example, $-5.394\ldots$, the trailing dots denoting further digits to whatever degree of precision is appropriate. The sign before a number is either $+$ or $-$. By convention, the $+$ sign is often omitted when the number is positive. However, the $-$ sign should *never* be omitted from a negative number. The number written as 2.568, and referred to as 'two point five six eight', is the integer, 2, plus five tenths plus six hundredths plus eight thousandths, or

$$2.568 = 2 + \frac{5}{10} + \frac{6}{100} + \frac{8}{1000}$$

The number -3.653 would be expanded as

$$-3.653 = -\left(3 + \frac{6}{10} + \frac{5}{100} + \frac{3}{1000}\right)$$

If a number has a value between -1 and $+1$, the integral part should be written as 0, as in 0.745 and -0.392. Writing such a number in the form .745 is bad practice and should be avoided, mainly because the decimal point is inconspicuous and can be easily missed. The inclusion of the 0's to the right of the decimal point is vital in a number such as 0.003. Written as a fraction, this number is

$$0.003 = \frac{3}{1000}$$

Similarly, the numbers 0.03 and 0.3 can be written in fractional form as

$$0.03 = \frac{3}{100} \quad \text{and} \quad 0.3 = \frac{3}{10}$$

Some fractional quantities are readily converted into decimal form by utilising the fact that the value of a fraction is unchanged when the top and bottom lines are multiplied by the same number. For example, a quarter is converted to decimal form by multiplying the top and bottom lines by 25:

$$\frac{1}{4} = \frac{25}{100} = 0.25$$

Note that 0.25 can be thought of as two tenths plus five hundredths, or as twenty-five hundredths:

$$0.25 = \frac{2}{10} + \frac{5}{100} = \frac{25}{100}$$

The decimal representations of some fractions should be committed to memory as they are of frequent occurrence:

$$\frac{1}{2} = 0.5, \quad \frac{1}{4} = 0.25, \quad \frac{3}{4} = 0.75, \quad \frac{1}{8} = 0.125 \qquad (1.1)$$

It is often useful to think of numbers as points on a line, or **axis**, with a scale attached. The numbers -3.653, -0.392, 0.745 and 2.568 could be represented as points on an axis as shown in Figure 1.1.

Figure 1.1

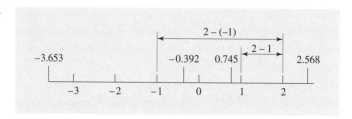

The values of the numbers increase on moving from left to right, 2.568 being a *larger* number than -3.653. Notice also that the result of subtracting 1 from 2 is equal to the distance from 1 to 2 on the axis, that is, 1 unit. Similarly, subtracting -1 from 2 gives a result that is equal to the distance from -1 to 2 along the axis, or 3 units:

$$2 - (-1) = 3$$

**Self test questions
1.1**

Write out the following numbers in decimal form:

(a) $2\frac{3}{10}$, (b) $1\frac{1}{5}$, (c) $-3\frac{7}{10}$, (d) $\frac{8}{100}$, (e) $-\frac{3}{4}$, (f) $1\frac{3}{8}$

Draw an axis, similar to that shown in Figure 1.1, and indicate approximately where these numbers would appear on it.

Decimal representation is the most commonly used method of denoting a number. Basic operations such as addition and multiplication can be carried out easily using an electronic calculator, and it is a simple matter to recognise the relative sizes of numbers written in this way. For example,

$$\frac{17}{25} = 0.68 \qquad \text{and} \qquad \frac{2}{3} = 0.67$$

but it is the decimal forms of these two fractions that make it clear that the first is larger than the second. However, decimal representation does have limitations. The second of the two fractions written above is only approximately represented by the decimal number 0.67. An attempt to find an accurate decimal representation would produce $0.666\,666\,666\ldots$, the string of 6's following the decimal point being without end. This feature of decimal representation is rarely a problem in practical calculations, but it does show that not all numbers can be expressed exactly in decimal form. Indeed, there are many numbers that cannot be expressed exactly in decimal form and cannot be expressed exactly in the form of any fraction that is written as one integer divided by another. The number pi (π) written to ten places of decimals has the value,

$$\pi = 3.141\,592\,6535\ldots \text{etc.}$$

This number cannot be written down exactly in decimal form and it cannot be written exactly as any fraction involving integers. Such numbers are referred to as **irrational numbers**

1.2   **Fractions**

The values of quantities are not usually specified in the form of fractions. For example, it would be more common for a mass to be referred to as

0.25 gram rather than $\frac{1}{4}$ gram, even though both have the same meaning. Simple arithmetic operations such as addition are generally more awkward with fractions, which is one reason why decimal representation is preferred. However, algebraic fractions containing variables rather than numbers occur often and for this reason it is important to understand such basic operations as the addition of fractions. The value of a fraction is obtained by dividing a number known as the **numerator** by another number known as the **denominator**:

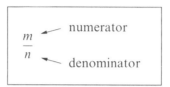

Addition and subtraction of fractions

A prerequisite of simple addition and subtraction is that *the quantities being added or subtracted must be of the same type*. A sum such as

$$\frac{2}{3} + \frac{3}{5}$$

is the same as

$$2 \times \left(\frac{1}{3}\right) + 3 \times \left(\frac{1}{5}\right)$$

and this cannot be evaluated immediately because the quantities being added, thirds and fifths, are not the same. However, as noted above, an important property of fractions is that we can multiply or divide the numerator and denominator by the same number and the fraction does not change in value. Fractions such as a third and a fifth can be converted into fractions with a **common denominator** as indicated below:

$$\frac{1}{3} = \frac{1 \times 5}{3 \times 5} = \frac{5}{15} \quad \text{and} \quad \frac{1}{5} = \frac{1 \times 3}{5 \times 3} = \frac{3}{15}$$

The sum can now be written as

$$\frac{2}{3} + \frac{3}{5} = 2 \times \left(\frac{5}{15}\right) + 3 \times \left(\frac{3}{15}\right)$$

$$= \frac{10}{15} + \frac{9}{15}$$

$$= \frac{19}{15}$$

The subtraction of fractions is done in a similar way:

$$\frac{2}{3} - \frac{3}{5} = \frac{10}{15} - \frac{9}{15} = \frac{1}{15}$$

The common denominator, 15, is a number into which both 3 and 5 will divide without remainder. Such a number can always be found simply by multiplying together the denominators of the fractions, although doing this does not always give the smallest common denominator. This example explains how we can convert dissimilar fractions into fractions of the same type in order to add or subtract them. The sequence of operations can be contracted into the cross multiplication procedure illustrated below to obtain the same result more quickly:

$$\frac{2}{3} + \frac{3}{5} = \frac{2 \times 5 + 3 \times 3}{3 \times 5}$$

$$= \frac{19}{15}$$

Subtraction of fractions can be done in a similar way but with the $-$ sign replacing the $+$ sign.

Self test questions

1.2

Carry out the following additions and subtractions

(a) $\frac{1}{2} + \frac{2}{3}$, (b) $\frac{1}{4} + \frac{1}{3}$, (c) $\frac{1}{2} - \frac{1}{6}$, (d) $\frac{5}{7} - \frac{1}{2}$, (e) $\frac{4}{9} - \frac{2}{3}$

Multiplication of fractions

Quantities that are added or subtracted must be of the same type, but this is not required for multiplication. A half of a third is a sixth:

$$\frac{1}{2} \times \frac{1}{3} = \frac{1}{6}$$

To obtain this result, we simply multiply together the denominators, 2 and 3, to obtain the denominator in the resulting fraction. The numerator in a product is also the product of the numerators in the fractions being multiplied together:

$$\frac{4}{5} \times \frac{2}{3} = \frac{8}{15}$$

In the evaluation of a product such as

$$\frac{4}{5} \times \frac{3}{8}$$

the numerator of the first fraction and the denominator of the second can be divided by 4 to give the simplified product

$$\frac{1}{5} \times \frac{3}{2}$$

**Self test questions
1.3**

Multiply out the following products of fractions

(a) $\frac{2}{5} \times \frac{3}{2}$, (b) $\frac{5}{7} \times \frac{2}{3}$, (c) $\frac{3}{8} \times \frac{4}{5}$, (d) $\frac{1}{3} \times \frac{5}{7}$

Reciprocal of a fraction

The **reciprocal** of a number n is defined by

$$\text{reciprocal of } n = \frac{1}{n}$$

The value of this quantity is found by dividing n into 1. The reciprocal of a fraction such as a quarter is 4 since there are four quarters in 1:

$$\frac{1}{1/4} = 4$$

In general, the reciprocal of a fraction is obtained by **inverting** the fraction

$$\frac{1}{m/n} = \frac{n}{m}$$

1.3	Large and small numbers

A standard way of writing down a large number is, for example, 1.26×10^9. This number is 1260 000 000, but writing it down like this should be avoided. Apart from taking up unnecessary space, it is hard to appreciate quickly how large the number is without counting all the 0's, and the number is difficult to remember. Similar criticisms could be made of writing down a small number as, for example, 0.000 000 0154. This would be better written as 1.54×10^{-8}. The number 1.26×10^9 would be referred to as 'one point two six times ten to the power of nine' and 1.54×10^{-8} would be 'one point five four times ten to the power of minus eight'. In computer programs and on some calculators, the same number would appear as 1.54E − 8, in which 'E − 8' represents $\times 10^{-8}$. The power, $\times 10^9$, would appear as 'E9'.

Powers of 10

A number written as 10^3, and referred to as 'ten to the power of three', is the same as $10 \times 10 \times 10$, or 1000. The **exponent**, 3 in this case, is equal to the number of 0's following the 1 in 1000. Other examples are given below:

$$10 = 10^1, \qquad 100 = 10^2, \qquad 1000 = 10^3, \qquad 10{,}000 = 10^4, \ldots \text{etc.}$$

If we multiply 100 by 1000 we obtain 100 000, or 10^5:

$$10^2 \times 10^3 = 10^5$$

It is generally true that to multiply together two powers of ten, we add their exponents. The general rule is

$$10^m \times 10^n = 10^{(m+n)} \tag{1.1}$$

If we divide 1000 by 100 we obtain 10 or 10^1:

$$\frac{10^3}{10^2} = 10^1$$

and it is generally true that

$$\frac{10^m}{10^n} = 10^{(m-n)} \tag{1.2}$$

This leads to a surprising result when the numbers m and n are equal. For example, if they are both equal to 2, we obtain,

$$\frac{10^2}{10^2} = 10^{(2-2)} = 10^0$$

However, 10^2 is 100 and we know that 100 divided by 100 should be equal to 1. It must be the case, therefore, that 10^0 is equal to 1. In fact, it is true that any number raised to the power of 0 has a value of 1:

$$a^0 = 1 \tag{1.3}$$

where a is any positive or negative number.

Negative exponents

Powers of 10 that have values less than 1 have negative exponents:

$$10^{-1} = \frac{1}{10} = 0.1, \quad 10^{-2} = \frac{1}{100} = 0.01, \quad 10^{-3} = \frac{1}{1000} = 0.001, \ldots \text{etc.}$$

This notation is consistent with the rules for multiplying and dividing powers of 10. For example,

$$1000 \times \frac{1}{1000} = 1 \quad \text{and} \quad 10^3 \times 10^{-3} = 10^{(3-3)} = 10^0 = 1$$

In general, for any number, a,

$$a^{-2} = \frac{1}{a^2}, \qquad a^{-3} = \frac{1}{a^3}, \ldots \text{etc.}$$

Note that

$$\frac{10^4}{10^{-3}} = 10^{(4--3)}$$

which is the same as $10^{(4+3)}$ or 10^7.

**Self test questions
1.4**

Evaluate the following:

(a) $(2.5 \times 10^3) \times (3 \times 10^2)$, (b) $(4 \times 10^6) \times (2 \times 10^4)$,

(c) $\dfrac{4 \times 10^5}{2 \times 10^3}$, (d) $\dfrac{5 \times 10^3}{2 \times 10^7}$, (e) $\dfrac{2 \times 10^6}{4 \times 10^{-3}}$

Expressing numbers in standard form

Writing the number 1260 000 000 as 1.26×10^9 is described as writing it in **standard form**. A number expressed in this way has a single digit to the left of the decimal point. The power of ten used is found by counting the number of places by which the decimal point located at the end of the number must be moved to the left as indicated below:

9 places

$$1\,260\,000\,000 = 1.26 \times 10^9$$

The number 0.000 000 0154 is converted to standard form by moving the decimal point *eight places to the right* so that it follows the first non-zero digit, and then multiplying by 10^{-8}:

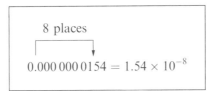

8 places

$$0.000\,000\,0154 = 1.54 \times 10^{-8}$$

Very large and very small numbers should be written in standard form. Numbers written as 0.04 or 53.5 or 1250 are not in standard form, but they are acceptable because they are compact and are unlikely to cause confusion. However, a number written as 0.000 000 28 is clearly more difficult to handle and it should be written as 2.8×10^{-7}.

Self test questions 1.5

Write the following numbers in standard form:

(a) 1280 000 (b) 528 000 (c) 0.000 0035 (d) 0.000 000 000 0879

Addition and subtraction of numbers written in standard form

The result of adding the numbers 1.34×10^3 and 4.242×10^5 is found by first expressing both numbers to the same power of 10. In order to obtain a result that is in standard form, we would write 1.34×10^3 as a number written to a power of 5:

$$1.34 \times 10^3 = 0.0134 \times 10^5$$

Increasing the power of 10 from 10^3 to 10^5 has been compensated for by moving the decimal point two places to the left. The numbers can now be added directly:

$$4.242 \times 10^5 + 0.0134 \times 10^5 = 4.2554 \times 10^5$$

Subtraction of numbers written in standard form proceeds in a similar way with the + sign replaced by a − sign.

Self test questions 1.6

Evaluate the following:

(a) $7.34 \times 10^4 + 2.5 \times 10^3$, (b) $6.95 \times 10^6 - 4 \times 10^4$,
(c) $3.422 \times 10^{-3} + 6.3 \times 10^{-6}$

Table 1.1	Prefix	Symbol	Power of ten	Example
Prefixes	pico	p	10^{-12}	picosecond, ps, 10^{-12} s
	nano	n	10^{-9}	nanometre, nm, 10^{-9} m
	micro	μ	10^{-6}	micromole, μmol, 10^{-6} mol
	milli	m	10^{-3}	millilitre, mL, 10^{-3} L
	kilo	k	10^{3}	kilogram, kg, 10^{3} g
	mega	M	10^{6}	megavolt, MV, 10^{6} V
	giga	G	10^{9}	gigahertz, GHz, 10^{9} Hz

1.4   The use of prefixes

Instead of referring to a mass as being 0.024 gram, we could write it as 24 milligrams, a milligram being one thousandth of a gram. Prefixes such as milli are widely used as a means of specifying the size of a quantity in a manageable form. Some of the more commonly used prefixes are given in Table 1.1.

Two other prefixes are frequently encountered; centi, meaning one hundredth, as in centimetre, and deci, meaning one tenth, as in decimetre, but these two prefixes are applied only to a limited number of units. The use of prefixes in the specification of some quantities is well established by convention. For example, the wavelength of green light is approximately 5×10^{-7} metre, but usually this would be written as 500 nm (nanometre). This example exposes an ambiguity in the use of prefixes in that 500 nm could also be written as 0.5 μm, but this latter notation, although correct, is less commonly used to specify a wavelength in the visible region of the spectrum.

Self test questions 1.7

Rewrite the following quantities using the appropriate prefixes

(a) 6.5×10^{-6} g, (b) 2.8×10^{-3} s, (c) 45 000 J (joule), (d) 2.5×10^{-5} mol

1.5   Significant figures

All measurements are limited in the precision that can be attained. If an object was weighed on a balance and the reading was found to fluctuate between 2.845 g and 2.855 g, then the result should be recorded as 2.85 g. Writing the number in this way does not mean that we are certain that the third digit is 5. However, figures added to the right of the third digit would be unreliable and 2.85 g would be the best result that could be obtained under the circumstances. We would say that the mass had been determined to three **significant figures**. The same result could be expressed in different ways. For example, it could be written as 0.002 85 kg or as 2850 mg, but it would still be precise to three significant figures, the 0's being added simply to establish the position of the decimal point. However, writing the mass as 2850 mg is ambiguous. It could mean that the zero has been added simply to locate the decimal point, or it could mean that the fourth digit can be measured precisely and just happens to be zero. In the first case, the number would be precise to three significant figures and in the second case, to four. This ambiguity could be avoided by writing the number as 2.85×10^3 mg, which is expressed to three significant figures. The number 2.850×10^3 is expressed to four significant figures; the last one just happens to be zero. The following examples indicate the number of significant figures implied by the way in which a number is expressed:

1.002	four significant figures
0.002	one significant figure
1.5850	five significant figures; the final zero is significant here
1.765×10^6	four significant figures

Whenever measurements, or numbers derived from measurements, are quoted, it is important to express them to an appropriate number of significant figures.

Finding the number of significant figures when numbers are added or subtracted

Consider three volumes which, to the correct number of significant figures, have values of $23.1 \, \text{cm}^3$, $1.24 \, \text{cm}^3$ and $144 \, \text{cm}^3$. Each of these values is written to three significant figures and, in each case, the final digit is uncertain. However, the final digit in $144 \, \text{cm}^3$ represents a whole number of cm^3, whereas $1.24 \, \text{cm}^3$ is written to two places of decimals and its final digit is a multiple of $0.01 \, \text{cm}^3$. Clearly, the uncertainty in the number $144 \, \text{cm}^3$ will have the dominant effect as it is greater than the uncertainties in the other two. *When adding these values together, the number of decimal places in the result should be the same as the smallest number of decimal places in the quantities being added.* The result would be

$$23.1 + 1.24 + 144 = 168.34 \, \text{cm}^3$$

which should be written as $168 \, \text{cm}^3$ to the correct number of decimal places. The same rule is used to determine the number of decimal places in a quantity found by subtracting measured values.

Finding the number of significant figures when numbers are multiplied or divided

The method used to determine the appropriate number of significant figures in quantities that result from multiplication is illustrated by the example below.

If the sides of a rectangle were measured to be 1.25 cm and 3.225 cm then the area of the rectangle would be found from

$$\text{area} = 1.25 \times 3.225 = 4.031\,25\,\text{cm}^2$$

The result of this calculation is what is produced by a calculator, but it implies a degree of precision greater than that suggested in the numbers from which it was derived. The number 1.25 is written to three significant figures and 3.225 is written to four. The result of the multiplication should not be written to more significant figures than the least precise of these two numbers, that is, it should not be written to more than three significant figures. This means that the result should be quoted as 4.03 cm². *The number of significant figures in the result is equal to the smallest number of significant figures in the quantities being multiplied together.* A similar rule applies when two numbers are divided. In the above example, the calculated number, 4.031 25, was truncated to 4.03 simply by dropping the last three digits. The convention adopted is that rounding a number in this way is acceptable provided that the fourth digit is less than 5. However, if this digit had been equal to or greater than 5, for example if the result of the calculation had been 4.036 25, then the number would have been truncated by rounding up to give 4.04.

**Self test questions
1.8**

How many significant figures are implied by the representation of the following numbers?

(a) 2.15, (b) 3.08, (c) 0.06, (d) 0.060, (e) 4.850, (f) 1.62×10^3

1.6 | **Units of measurement**

Attempting to specify the size of a quantity merely by quoting a number would not be adequate in most cases. In addition, it would be necessary to

Table 1.2	Property	Base unit	Symbol
SI base units	mass	kilogram	kg
	length	metre	m
	time	second	s
	temperature	kelvin	K
	amount of substance	mole	mol
	electric current	ampere	A
	luminous intensity	candela	cd

specify the unit in which the quantity is measured. For example, to state that the mass of an object is 1.28 is meaningless without also stating the unit (milligram, gram, kilogram, ...) to which this number refers. A few quantities have no associated unit and in these cases quoting a number on its own is enough. This is true of quantities such as refractive index, optical absorbance, and mole ratio. However, most quantities encountered in chemistry will have units and *these units should always be clearly stated.*

Some fundamentally different quantities can often be expressed using the same underlying unit. For example, length and area refer to different properties of an object, but a length could be specified in metres (m) and an area in square metres (m^2).

The unit of area is derived from the unit of length, the metre. The connection between the unit of length and the unit of area arises from the fact that an area is *defined* as the quantity obtained by multiplying together two lengths. For example, the area of a rectangle is obtained by multiplying together the lengths of its longer and shorter sides. However, there are no similar connections between mass and length or between temperature and length, so the units of mass and temperature cannot be written in terms of the unit of length; other types of unit are required. Fortunately, the units of physical properties of interest in science can be constructed from a small number of **base units** that are given in Table 1.2.

The base units in this table are those adopted in the internationally used SI (Système International) system.

Derived units

Physical properties that are not listed in Table 1.2 have units *derived* from those that are listed. For example, the volume of a rectangular solid object is found from

volume = length × width × height

As length, width and height can all be specified in metres, the unit of volume is

$$\text{unit of volume} = 1\,\text{m} \times 1\,\text{m} \times 1\,\text{m} = 1\,\text{m}^3$$

We would say that the unit of volume is the metre cubed, or m^3, and it is derived from the unit of length. The metre cubed is a large unit for many purposes and volume is often specified in smaller units. The centimetre cubed is the volume of a cube with sides 1 cm in length and it is denoted by cm^3 (note that cm^3 really means $(cm)^3$) . However, this unit is still defined as the product of three lengths. Sometimes, derived units are given special names. In the case of units of volume, the litre is defined as being $1000\,cm^3$ and it is denoted by the symbol L.

More complex derived units are constructed from a consideration of how the property concerned is defined. For example, we could define the rate of flow of water through a pipe as the volume of water that passes through the pipe in one second. A measurement of this quantity in a particular case could reveal that 16 litres of water flows through the pipe in an interval of 10 seconds. The rate of flow would then be given by:

$$\text{rate of flow} = \frac{16}{10} = 1.6 \text{ litre per second}$$

Here, we have to *divide* a volume by a time to obtain the required result. The unit for rate of flow could therefore be written as

$$\text{litre per second} = \frac{\text{L}}{\text{s}} \text{ or L s}^{-1}$$

Three derived SI units commonly encountered in chemistry are given in Table 1.3

To understand where these units come from we must first note that the unit of velocity is metre per second (m s^{-1}), and that acceleration is defined as the change in velocity per unit time, so that the unit of acceleration is given by

$$\text{unit of acceleration} = \frac{\text{m s}^{-1}}{\text{s}} \quad \text{or} \quad \text{m s}^{-2}$$

Newton's second law of motion defines a force as a mass multiplied by an acceleration, making the SI unit of force kg m s^{-2}. Energy has the same

Table 1.3 Units of force, energy and pressure	Name of unit	Unit of	Symbol	Base units
	newton	force	N	kg m s^{-2}
	joule	energy	J	$\text{kg m}^2\,\text{s}^{-2}$ or N m
	pascal	pressure	Pa	$\text{kg m}^{-1}\,\text{s}^{-2}$ or N m^{-2}

unit as work, which is defined as the product of a force and a distance, making the SI unit of energy $kg\,m\,s^{-2} \times m$ or $kg\,m^2\,s^{-2}$. This unit is also written as $N\,m$, or 'newton metre'. A pressure is a force per unit area with the unit $N\,m^{-2}$, or 'newton per metre squared'.

Self test questions
1.9

(a) An object moving with constant speed covers a distance of $1.5\,m$ in $0.3\,s$. What is the velocity of the object?

(b) The velocity of an object moving in a straight line changes from $5\,m\,s^{-1}$ to $10\,m\,s^{-1}$ in $0.2\,s$. What is the acceleration of the object? If the mass of the object is $0.1\,kg$, what force is required to give it this acceleration?

Conversion of units

The outcome of calculations depends critically upon using appropriate units for quantities that appear in those calculations. This often requires that a quantity specified in one type of unit be converted to some other unit. In order to understand what is involved in conversion of units from one type to another it is necessary to consider what is meant by stating, for example, that a length is $2.8\,m$. We can write $2.8\,m$ as follows:

$$2.8\,m = 2.8 \times 1\,m$$

It is a pure number, 2.8, multiplied by a length of $1\,m$. If we wanted to convert this into centimetres, we note that $1\,m = 100\,cm$ and simply insert $100\,cm$ in place of $1\,m$:

$$2.8\,m = 2.8 \times 100\,cm$$
$$= 280\,cm$$

To convert an area of $3.5\,m^2$ to cm^2 we note that $3.5\,m^2$ can be written as:

$$3.5\,m^2 = 3.5 \times 1\,m \times 1\,m \quad \text{or} \quad 3.5 \times (1\,m)^2$$

Again, inserting $100\,cm$ in place of $1\,m$ gives:

$$3.5\,m^2 = 3.5 \times 100\,cm \times 100\,cm = 3.5 \times 10^4 cm^2$$

(note that $1\,m^2$ is $10^4\,cm^2$, *not* $100\,cm^2$ and that $1\,m^3$ is $10^6\,cm^3$, *not* $100\,cm^3$).

A more complicated example involves converting a density from gram per centimetre cubed $(g\,cm^{-3})$ to kilogram per metre cubed $(kg\,m^{-3})$. The density of copper is $8.9 \, \text{g cm}^{-3}$. We can write this in the form

$$\text{density of copper} = 8.9 \times \frac{1\text{g}}{1 \, \text{cm} \times 1 \, \text{cm} \times 1 \, \text{cm}}$$

1 g is one thousandth of a kilogram or 10^{-3} kg, and 1 cm is one hundredth of a metre or 10^{-2} m. Inserting these values into the above expression gives:

$$\text{density of copper} = 8.9 \times \frac{10^{-3} \, \text{kg}}{10^{-2} \, \text{m} \times 10^{-2} \, \text{m} \times 10^{-2} \, \text{m}}$$

$$= 8.9 \times \frac{10^{-3} \, \text{kg}}{10^{-6} \, \text{m}^3}$$

$$= 8.9 \times 10^3 \, \text{kg m}^{-3}$$

Self test questions
1.10

(a) The heat released when methane undergoes combustion at constant pressure is 890 kilojoule per mole (kJ mol^{-1}). Express this quantity in units of joule per gram (J g^{-1}). Assume that 1 mole of methane has a mass of 16 grams.

(b) Standard atmospheric pressure is 101.325 kilopascal per metre squared (kPa m^{-2}). Express this quantity in units of pascal per centimetre squared (Pa cm^{-2}).

Dimensions

The dimensions of a physical property refer to the kind of property it is; for example, whether it is a length, an area, a mass or, perhaps, a combination of these. In the sense used here, the dimensions of a quantity are in no way related to its size. The basic properties of mass, length and time have dimensions denoted by M, L and T. (Care must be taken to avoid confusing L, the dimension of length, with L denoting the litre. Also, the dimension of time, T, must not be confused with temperature.) An area, which is obtained by multiplying a length by another length, would be said to have dimensions of length squared, or L^2. This would be written as

$$[\text{area}] = L^2$$

in which [area] represents the dimensions of area. The notion of the dimensions of area is a more general concept than that of the units in which area is specified, as the units of area can have several forms such as m^2, cm^2, ... etc. A volume would be said to have dimensions of L^3, and a density, which is obtained by dividing a mass by a volume, would have dimensions of $M L^{-3}$. Each of the basic quantities listed in Table 1.2 has an independent dimension associated with it. Here, we will denote the dimension corresponding to temperature by θ and the dimension corresponding to amount of substance by α.

Self test questions
1.11

(a) The concentration of solution is the amount of solute per unit volume of solution. What are the dimensions of concentration?
(b) Power has the dimensions of energy expended per unit time. What are the dimensions of power? (See Table 1.3 for the units of energy.)

It is not intended to explore the subject of dimensional analysis, but the relevance of dimensions to equations should be noted. In any equation containing physical properties, the two sides of the equation should not only have the same value, they should also have the same dimensions. Suppose that, in an investigation of a chemical reaction taking place in solution, it is found that, in the early stages of the reaction, the concentration of one of the reactants increases with time according to

concentration, $c = $ constant $\times$ time

or

$$c = kt,$$

in which k denotes the constant.

Concentration has dimensions of amount of substance divided by volume, or αL^{-3}. However, time has dimensions of T. The only way in which we can ensure that the left and right sides of this equation have the same dimensions is to require that the constant, k, has dimensions determined from:

$$\alpha L^{-3} = [k] \times T$$

This relationship between dimensions is satisfied if k has dimensions of $\alpha L^{-3} T^{-1}$, or

$$[k] = \alpha L^{-3} T^{-1}$$

If the units corresponding to the dimensions α, L and T are mole, metre and second, then the unit of k would be $\text{mol m}^{-3}\,\text{s}^{-1}$.

An equation that occurs when absorption spectrometry is used to study light-absorbing solutions is

$$A = \varepsilon cl$$

in which A is absorbance, c is concentration, l is path length and ε is referred to as the extinction coefficient or molar absorptivity. Absorbance is a measure of the extent to which a solution absorbs light of a particular wavelength, and this equation shows how absorbance is related to the concentration of light-absorbing solute and the length of the light path through the solution. Because of the way in which absorbance is defined, it has no dimensions; it is said to be *dimensionless* and would be written down simply as a number without units. The dimensions of a dimensionless quantity are denoted by the number 1. Note that L^0, M^0, and T^0 are equal to 1. The dimensional form of the above equation would be

$$[A] = [\varepsilon c l] = 1$$

The concentration c has dimensions of αL^{-3} and l has dimensions L giving

$$1 = [\varepsilon]\alpha L^{-3} \times L = [\varepsilon]\alpha L^{-2}$$

or

$$[\varepsilon] = \alpha^{-1}L^2$$

With amount of substance specified in moles and length in metres, the unit of ε would be $mol^{-1}\,m^2$. However, the units in which ε is expressed in practice are often more complicated than this. Concentration is conventionally specified in moles per litre, or $mol\,L^{-1}$, and the path length is often specified in centimetres, simply because the cells used to hold the solution in an absorption spectrometer often have a pathlength of 1 cm. As in the case of dimensions, we can represent the units of the dimensionless quantity, absorbance, by 1 and determine the conventional units of ε from the relationship

$$1 = (\text{unit of } \varepsilon) \times (mol\,L^{-1}) \times (cm)$$

giving *unit* of $\varepsilon = mol^{-1}\,L\,cm^{-1}$. However, the *dimensions* of ε are still $\alpha^{-1}L^2$.

1.7	Percentages

A number expressed as a percentage is simply a particular kind of fraction in which the denominator is 100. If, in a group of five people, two had blue eyes and three had brown eyes then

$$\text{fraction of the total with blue eyes} = \frac{2}{5}$$

To convert this fraction into a percentage we would simply multiply it by 100:

$$\text{percentage of people with blue eyes} = \frac{2}{5} \times 100 = 40\%$$

Assuming that our group of five is representative, we would expect approximately 40 people from a group of 100 to have blue eyes. Percentages do not have units. They appear in a wide variety of contexts and, in chemistry, they are often used to denote the **yield** of a chemical reaction. The yield of a chemical reaction refers to the amount of product that is formed. Usually, reactions do not produce the maximum yield possible for several reasons, such as that not all of the reactants react, that is, the reaction does not go to completion. For example, if 20 g of benzene reacted with an excess of nitric acid to produce nitrobenzene, we would expect to obtain approximately 31.5 g of nitrobenzene if the reaction went to completion.

$$C_6H_6 + HNO_3 \longrightarrow C_6H_5NO_2 + H_2O$$

1 mol	1 mol	1 mol	1 mol
78.1 g		123.1 g	

1 mol of benzene (78.1 g) would be expected to produce 1 mol (123.1 g) of nitrobenzene, so 20 g of benzene should produce

$$123.1 \times \frac{20}{78.1} \text{ g of nitrobenzene}$$

To three significant figures, this comes to 31.5 g. If, in an actual preparation, it was found that only 22.5 g of nitrobenzene was produced, we would say that the yield of the reaction was

$$\text{yield} = \frac{\text{actual amount of product formed}}{\text{maximum possible amount of product}} \times 100$$

$$= \frac{22.5}{31.5} \times 100$$

$$= 71.4\%$$

**Self test questions
1.12**

Convert the following fractions to percentages:

(a) $\frac{3}{4}$, (b) $\frac{3}{5}$, (c) $\frac{28}{500}$, (d) $\frac{5}{80}$

Answers **to self test questions**

1.1   (a) 2.3, (b) 1.2, (c) -3.7, (d) 0.08, (e) -0.75, (f) 1.375

1.2 (a) $\frac{7}{6}$, (b) $\frac{7}{12}$, (c) $\frac{1}{3}$, (d) $\frac{3}{14}$, (e) $-\frac{2}{9}$

1.3 (a) $\frac{3}{5}$, (b) $\frac{10}{21}$, (c) $\frac{3}{10}$, (d) $\frac{5}{21}$

1.4 (a) 7.5×10^5, (b) 8×10^{10}, (c) 2×10^2, (d) 2.5×10^{-4}, (e) 5×10^8

1.5 (a) 1.28×10^6, (b) 5.28×10^5, (c) 3.5×10^{-6}, (d) 8.79×10^{-11}

1.6 (a) 7.59×10^4, (b) 6.91×10^6, (c) 3.4283×10^{-3}

1.7 (a) $6.5\,\mu\text{g}$, (b) $2.8\,\text{ms}$, (c) $45\,\text{kJ}$, (d) $25\,\mu\text{mol}$

1.8 (a) three, (b) three, (c) one, (d) two, (e) four, (f) three

1.9 (a) $5\,\text{m s}^{-1}$, (b) $25\,\text{m s}^{-2}$, $2.5\,\text{N}$

1.10 (a) $5.5625 \times 10^4\,\text{J g}^{-1}$, (b) $10.1325\,\text{Pa cm}^{-2}$

1.11 (a) αL^{-3}, (b) $\text{M L}^2\,\text{T}^{-3}$

1.12 (a) 75%, (b) 60%, (c) 5.6%, (d) 6.25%

Questions **on Chapter 1**

1.1 Write out the following numbers in order of increasing size:
$$10^6, -0.12, 0.004, -2 \times 10^3, 4.8 \times 10^{-4}, 3.2 \times 10^3, 4000, 6 \times 10^{-6}$$

1.2 Evaluate the following, writing the answers in the form of fractions:
(a) $1\frac{2}{5} + \frac{1}{3}$, (b) $2\frac{1}{3} - 1\frac{5}{6}$, (c) $\frac{2}{3} + \frac{1}{6} + \frac{5}{12}$, (d) $\frac{2}{3} + \frac{7}{12} - \frac{1}{6}$

1.3 Evaluate the following, writing the answers in the form of fractions:
(a) $\frac{4}{5} \times \frac{2}{3}$, (b) $1\frac{1}{3} \times \frac{6}{8}$, (c) $\dfrac{1}{\frac{1}{4} + \frac{1}{3}}$, (d) $\dfrac{1}{\frac{1}{5} + \frac{1}{2}} - \dfrac{3}{7}$

1.4 Evaluate the following, writing the answers in standard form:
(a) $(2.2 \times 10^4) \times (3 \times 10^2)$, (b) $(1.2 \times 10^6) \times (5 \times 10^{-3})$,
(c) $(4.7 \times 10^{-7}) \times (2 \times 10^3)$, (d) $(3.4 \times 10^{-3}) \times (3 \times 10^{-4})$

1.5 Evaluate the following, writing the answers in standard form:
(a) $\dfrac{7.5 \times 10^6}{3 \times 10^4}$, (b) $\dfrac{8.6 \times 10^4}{4 \times 10^6}$, (c) $\dfrac{6.9 \times 10^3}{3 \times 10^{-4}}$, (d) $\dfrac{3.2 \times 10^{-6}}{2 \times 10^3}$

1.6 Write out the following lengths in order of increasing size:
$0.1\,\text{mm}$, $740\,\text{nm}$, $0.02\,\text{cm}$, $0.8\,\mu\text{m}$, $0.5\,\text{nm}$, $600\,\text{pm}$, $150\,\mu\text{m}$

1.7 Determine the number of significant figures implied in the following quantities:
(a) 0.034m, (b) $15.00\,\text{g}$, (c) $2.8 \times 10^{-2}\,\text{cm}^3$, (d) $2.020\,\text{cm}$

1.8 Three objects have masses which, when specified to an appropriate number of significant figures, are 9.80 g, 0.322 g, and 0.012 g. Write down the total mass to the appropriate number of significant figures.

1.9 A solution is prepared by dissolving 0.14 mol of solute in the solvent so as to make 0.300 L of solution. Calculate the concentration of the solution in $mol\,L^{-1}$ and write down the result to an appropriate number of significant figures.

1.10 Write down the following numbers to three significant figures:

(a) 2643, (b) 1218, (c) 0.034 61, (d) 4.735×10^{-3}, (e) 1.200

1.11 Convert the following values into the units specified:

(a) 0.2 m into mm, (b) 632 nm into μm, (c) 1.2 g into kg, (d) 15 μs into ms

1.12 Convert the following values into the units specified:

(a) $0.65\,m^2$ into cm^2, (b) $0.5\,mm^2$ into m^2, (c) $0.2\,m^3$ into m^3, (d) $2\,cm^3$ into m^3

1.13 The Ångstrom (Å) is a unit of length sometimes used to specify the size of atoms. If 1 Å is equal to 1×10^{-10} m and the radius of an atom of sodium is 1.57 Å, what is the radius of a sodium atom in cm, nm and pm?

Assuming that a sodium atom is spherical and given that the volume of a sphere is $\frac{4}{3}\pi r^3$, in which r denotes the radius, calculate the volume of a sodium atom in cm^3, nm^3 and pm^3. Write down your answers in standard form and to three significant figures.

1.14 Convert the following quantities into the units specified:

(a) $0.25\,mol\,L^{-1}$ into $\mu mol\,mL^{-1}$, (b) $4.8\,g\,cm^{-3}$ into $kg\,m^{-3}$, (c) 2.5 L into m^3, (d) $10\,\mu g\,cm^{-2}$ into $g\,m^{-2}$

1.15 (a) Density is defined as mass per unit volume. What are the dimensions of density?

(b) The momentum of a moving object is defined as the mass of the body multiplied by its velocity. What are the dimensions of momentum?

1.16 The amount of heat absorbed by n mol of a gas when its temperature rises by an amount ΔT kelvin can be written as:

heat absorbed, $\Delta Q = nC\Delta T$

in which ΔQ is expressed in joules and C is known as the molar heat capacity relevant to the conditions under which the gas is heated;

usually either at constant pressure or at constant volume. Determine the unit in which C is expressed.

1.17 One effect of a particular chemical reaction that occurs in the solution state is to cause the volume of solution to increase slightly as the reaction proceeds. An investigation of this effect over the early stage of the reaction leads to the conclusion that the volume of the solution, V, depends upon time according to the empirical relationship:

$$V = a + bt$$

in which t represents time and a and b are constants. What are the dimensions of a and b? If V is measured in cm^3 and t in s, what are the units of a and b?

1.18 From the data given in Table 1.3, determine the dimensions of force, energy and pressure. What are the dimensions of the product PV, in which P denotes pressure and V denotes volume?

1.19 The pressure, P, volume, V, and temperature, T, of an ideal gas are related by the equation

$$PV = nRT$$

in which n is the number of moles of gas, R is a constant and T is measured in kelvin. If P is measured in $N\,m^{-2}$ (or Pa) and V in m^3, show that the unit of R can be written as $J\,mol^{-1}\,K^{-1}$.

1 mol of an ideal gas occupies a volume of 22.414 litre when the pressure of the gas is 101.325 kPa and the temperature is 273.15 K (0°C). Calculate the value of R in units of $J\,mol^{-1}\,K^{-1}$ from this data, expressing your answer to four significant figures.

1.20 Aspirin, $C_9H_8O_4$, can be prepared by the reaction of salicylic acid, $C_7H_6O_3$, with excess acetic anhydride, $C_4H_6O_3$, according to the reaction

$$2C_7H_6O_3 + C_4H_6O_3 \longrightarrow 2C_9H_8O_4 + H_2O$$

If 39 g of aspirin is produced in a reaction involving 50 g of salicylic acid, calculate the percentage yield for the reaction.

2 Logarithmic, exponential and trigonometric functions

We know that numbers such as 10, 100, 1000, ..., 0.1, 0.01, etc. can be written in the form 10^n where n is a positive or negative integer. For example, $10 = 10^1$, $100 = 10^2$, $0.01 = 10^{-2}$, and so on. But what meaning can be attached to 10^n when n is not an integer? That some meaning can be attached to such numbers is indicated by the rule for multiplying powers of 10. A value for the number $10^{\frac{1}{2}}$ can be found by considering the product $10^{\frac{1}{2}} \times 10^{\frac{1}{2}}$. The rule for multiplying powers of 10, $10^m \times 10^n = 10^{m+n}$, suggests that this product should be equal to $10^{\frac{1}{2}+\frac{1}{2}}$, which is 10^1 or simply 10. We conclude that $10^{\frac{1}{2}}$ is a number which when multiplied by itself gives the result 10. In other words, $10^{\frac{1}{2}}$ is the square root of 10 which, to four places of decimals, is 3.1623:

$$10^{\frac{1}{2}} = \sqrt{10} = 3.1623, \qquad \text{approximately}$$

In a similar way, we can show that $10^{\frac{1}{3}}$ is the cube root of 10, $\sqrt[3]{10}$ or 2.1544. The point of these calculations is to show that values for 10^n can be found when n is not integral. Any positive number can be written in the form $N = 10^n$, provided that we allow n to have non-integral values. For example, $23.5 = 10^{1.371}$. This is another way of writing down a number in addition to those discussed in Chapter 1.

Any positive number, N, can be written as $N = 10^n$

This method of expressing numbers is not restricted to the **base** number 10. We could write any positive number in the form $N = 2^n$ or $N = 12^n$ or, in general, $N = b^n$ in which b is any number that we choose to use as a base number. For the same number N, the required values of n

would be different for each value of b chosen. In practice, only two base numbers are in common use. One is the number 10 and the other is the irrational number, e. To ten decimal places, e has the value 2.718 281 8284. This may seem a strange choice of base number, but the number e appears naturally in the mathematical description of many physical phenomena, and its properties are less complex than its decimal expression implies.

2.1 Logarithms

When we write a number in the form $N = 10^n$, it is useful to have a name for the exponent, n, that this relationship associates with N. The exponent, n, is said to be the **logarithm** of N and it is denoted by $\log_{10} N$, the subscript, 10, indicating that the base number used is the number 10.

$$\text{If } N = 10^n, \text{ then } n = \log_{10} N \tag{2.1}$$

In words, $\log_{10} N$ is 'log to the base 10 of N'. Some examples of logarithms are:

$$\log_{10} 10 = 1, \qquad \log_{10} 100 = 2, \qquad \log_{10} 1000 = 3,$$

$$\log_{10} 0.01 = -2, \qquad \log_{10} 0.1 = -1$$

and, since $10^0 = 1$, $\log_{10} 1 = 0$. We would describe $\log_{10} N$ as a **function**; it is a prescription for calculating a number, n, from some other number, N.

Self test questions 2.1

Evaluate the following logarithms;

(a) $\log_{10} 10^5$, (b) $\log_{10} 10^{-7}$, (c) $\log_{10} 0.001$, (d) $\log_{10} \left(\dfrac{1}{10} \right)$

Logarithms of products and quotients

If we write the number M in the form 10^m and the number N as 10^n, then the product $M \times N$, or MN, can be written as

$$MN = 10^m \times 10^n = 10^{m+n}$$

From the definition of a logarithm, $\log_{10}(MN) = m + n = \log_{10} M + \log_{10} N$

$$\log_{10} MN = \log_{10} M + \log_{10} N \qquad (2.2)$$

A consequence of this relationship is that the logarithm of $M \times M$, or M^2, is given by

$$\log_{10} M^2 = \log_{10} M + \log_{10} M = 2 \log_{10} M$$

This can be extended to other, non-integral, powers of M, giving the result

$$\log_{10} M^P = p \log_{10} M \qquad (2.3)$$

For example, $\log_{10} 8^3 = 3 \log_{10} 8$, and $\log_{10} N^3 = 3 \log_{10} N$, where N is any positive number.

The logarithm of a quotient can be found in a similar way:

$$\frac{M}{N} = \frac{10^m}{10^n} = 10^{m-n}$$

From this we conclude that

$$\log_{10}\left(\frac{M}{N}\right) = m - n = \log_{10} M - \log_{10} N$$

$$\log_{10}\left(\frac{M}{N}\right) = \log_{10} M - \log_{10} N \qquad (2.4)$$

In practice, the logarithms of numbers would be calculated with the aid of a scientific calculator. However, the relationships given above, together with the fact that $\log_{10} 2$ is approximately equal to 0.3, can often be used to find approximate values for the logarithms of many numbers. For example, 20 is the same as 2×10, enabling us to write

$$\log_{10} 20 = \log_{10} 2 + \log_{10} 10 = 0.3 + 1 = 1.3, \qquad \text{approximately}$$

Similarly, 5 is 10 divided by 2 so that

$$\log_{10} 5 = \log_{10} 10 - \log_{10} 2 = 1 - 0.3 = 0.7, \qquad \text{approximately}$$

Self test questions

2.2

Calculate approximate values for the following logarithms given that $\log_{10} 2 = 0.3$ approximately:

(a) $\log_{10} 200$, (b) $\log_{10} 4$, (c) $\log_{10} 50$, (d) $\log_{10} 25$, (e) $\log_{10} 0.02$

Expressing a range of numbers in logarithmic form has the effect of compressing the range. This is evident from the list of numbers and their logarithmic forms given below:

N	10	100	1000	10 000	100 000	1000 000
$\log_{10} N$	1	2	3	4	5	6

Numbers are often expressed as logarithms simply to reduce the range of numbers involved to a more manageable scale. This is done with the pH scale of hydrogen ion concentrations introduced by the Danish chemist Søren Sørensen in 1909:

$$pH = -\log_{10} [H^+] \tag{2.5}$$

in which $[H^+]$ represents the concentration of hydrogen ions in a solution. Since the species H^+, a proton, is unlikely to exist in solution in an unattached state, it is sometimes denoted by H_3O^+ in recognition of the fact that it is expected to be associated with at least one water molecule, and pH is then written as

$$pH = -\log_{10}[H_3O^+] \tag{2.6}$$

Calculations involving pH are unaffected by which of these definitions is used and below, we will adopt the first. A solution in which the hydrogen ion concentration is $10^{-4} \, \text{mol} \, L^{-1}$ would have a pH given by

$$pH = -\log_{10} 10^{-4} = -(-4) = +4$$

Self test questions

2.3

Determine the pH values for solutions in which the hydrogen ion concentration is:

(a) $10^{-8} \, \text{mol} \, L^{-1}$, (b) $10^{-3} \, \text{mol} \, L^{-1}$, (c) $2 \times 10^{-3} \, \text{mol} \, L^{-1}$, (d) $4 \times 10^{-3} \, \text{mol} \, L^{-1}$

The range of values on the pH scale is often considered to extend from 0 to 14 corresponding to a range of hydrogen ion concentrations from $[H^+] = 1 \, \text{mol} \, L^{-1}$ to $[H^+] = 10^{-14} \, \text{mol} \, L^{-1}$. However, there is nothing to prevent the definition being extended beyond this range. For example, a solution in which $[H^+] = 10 \, \text{mol} \, L^{-1}$ would have a pH of -1 and one with $[H^+] = 10^{-15} \, \text{mol} \, L^{-1}$ would have a pH of 15, although it is unlikely that pH values in these extremes of the concentration range would have much significance. However, it should be noted that concentration has units and this raises the question: what are the units of pH? If we decide to include the units of concentration and write, for example, $pH = -\log_{10}(10^{-4} \, \text{mol} \, L^{-1})$, then we find that it is impossible to assign units to pH that are consistent with this expression. What is done in practice is to omit the unit, $\text{mol} \, L^{-1}$, and include only the numerical part as in $pH = -\log_{10} 10^{-4}$. This ensures that pH is dimensionless and has no units. However, dropping the units from a concentration merely because to include them would create problems suggests a defect in the definition of pH. Ideally, the quantity contained within a logarithmic function should not be one that requires units to be specified and a more satisfactory procedure, but not one that is adopted in practice, would be to define pH as

$$pH = -\log_{10} \frac{[H^+]}{[H^+]_0} \tag{2.7}$$

in which $[H^+]_0$ is the concentration of H^+ in some standard state chosen so that $[H^+]_0$ has the value $1 \, \text{mol} \, L^{-1}$. Although both $[H^+]$ and $[H^+]_0$ have units of concentration, the ratio

$$\frac{[H^+]}{[H^+]_0}$$

is dimensionless and the pH defined in this way is also dimensionless. Also, since $[H^+]_0$ has been chosen to be $1 \, \text{mol} \, L^{-1}$, the value of the pH so calculated would be identical to that calculated from $pH = -\log_{10}[H^+]$. This anomaly in the definition of pH does not lead to serious problems in practice, but in determining the appropriate units to be used in an equation that contains the logarithmic function, it should be borne in mind that the quantity within the logarithmic function should not have units. For example, in an equation such as

$$y = a + b \log_{10} x$$

the quantities y, a and b would all have the same units and x should be dimensionless.

Self test questions
2.4

(a) The ionic product of water, K_w, is defined by $K_w = [H^+][OH^-]$ and, when the concentrations $[H^+]$ and $[OH^-]$ are specified in $\text{mol} \, L^{-1}$, it has the value 10^{-14} at a temperature of 25°C. What is the value of $[OH^-]$ in a solution with a pH of 9 at 25°C?

(b)   Solution A has a pH of 3 and solution B has a pH of 5. Which
solution has the larger concentration of hydrogen ions?

2.2   Some general properties of exponents

The properties of logarithms have been derived from the properties of
numbers expressed as some power of 10. However, the base number
used need not be restricted to the number 10. The properties of numbers
expressed in the form 10^n are also found when some other base number is
used. For example, it is generally true that $b^m \times b^n = b^{m+n}$, in which b is
any base number. This is easily demonstrated when m and n are integers as
in $b^3 = b \times b \times b$ and $b^2 = b \times b$, so that $b^3 \times b^2 = b \times b \times b \times b \times b$,
which is b^5. It follows from this that

$$b^m \times b^m = b^{2m}$$

or,

$$(b^m)^2 = b^{2m}$$

In general,

$$b^{mn} = (b^m)^n = (b^n)^m$$

These relationships are also true for non-integral values of m and n. For
example,

$$b^{m/2} = (\sqrt{b})^m$$

It is also generally true that

$$\frac{b^m}{b^n} = b^{m-n}$$

This is easily established for integral values of m and n such as $m = 3$ and
$n = 2$ referred to above. This rule for division can be seen as an extension
of the first rule to negative exponents:

$$b^m \times b^{-n} = b^{m-n} \qquad \text{in which} \qquad b^{-n} = \frac{1}{b^n}$$

Just as we can write any positive number as some power of 10, we could also write it as $N = b^n$ in which b is any number that it is convenient to use as a base number.

<table>
<tr><td>**2.3**</td><td>**Natural logarithms**</td></tr>
</table>

In writing a number in the form $N = b^n$, a base number that is used extensively is the number e that was referred to earlier. To three places of decimals, e has the value 2.718. If we write the positive number, N, in the form

$$N = e^n$$

then the natural logarithm of N is equal to n, i.e. $n = \log_e N$. An alternative way of writing this is $n = \ln N$ in which 'ln' means the same as $\log_e$ or 'log to the base e'. We will use this second notation in this book.

$$\boxed{\text{If } N = e^n, \text{ then } n = \ln N} \tag{2.8}$$

The rules given earlier for logarithms to the base 10 also apply to natural logarithms. From the general properties of exponents described in Section 2.2 we know that

$$e^m \times e^n = e^{m+n}$$

If $M = e^m$ and $N = e^n$, then $\ln(MN) = m + n = \ln M + \ln N$. This and other similar relationships are given in equations (2.9) to (2.12) below. These rules are identical to those that apply to logarithms to the base 10.

$$\ln MN = \ln M + \ln N \tag{2.9}$$

$$\ln M^p = p \ln M \tag{2.10}$$

$$\ln \left(\frac{M}{N} \right) = \ln M - \ln N \tag{2.11}$$

$$\ln(1) = 0 \tag{2.12}$$

Logarithms to the base 10 are often used to compress a very wide range of numbers into a smaller range, as in the definition of pH. The choice of the base number 10 is convenient but arbitrary; other numbers could be used as the base. However, natural logarithms usually appear as the result of mathematical derivations. For example, the change in standard Gibbs free energy, ΔG^0, associated with a chemical reaction can be shown to be related to the equilibrium constant, K, for the reaction according to

$$\Delta G^0 = -RT \ln K \tag{2.13}$$

in which R is the gas constant and T the temperature in kelvin. Note that in this context, the symbol Δ is used to denote the *change* in a quantity as a result of a reaction occurring. This relationship is established in most texts on chemical thermodynamics. It should be noted that the equilibrium constant, K, that appears in equation (2.13) should be defined in such a way that it does not have units.

Self test questions
2.5

The equilibrium constant of a particular chemical reaction is 4.6×10^3 at a temperature of 298 K. Calculate the change in standard Gibbs free energy for the reaction at this temperature and specify the units in which it is expressed. ($R = 8.314 \, \mathrm{J \, K^{-1} \, mol^{-1}}$)

Conversion of natural logarithms to logarithms to base 10

Different types of logarithm of the same number will generally have different values:

$$\log_{10} p = q \tag{2.14}$$

and

$$\ln p = r \tag{2.15}$$

in which q and r are different except when $p = 1$. From equation (2.14), we can write p in the form $p = 10^q$ and then put this into equation (2.15):

$$\ln p = \ln(10^q) = q \ln 10, \qquad \text{see equation (2.10)}$$

The value of $\ln 10$ is approximately 2.303. Combining this with equation (2.14) establishes the following relationship between natural logarithms and logarithms to base 10:

$$\ln p = 2.303 \log_{10} p \tag{2.16}$$

2.4	**The exponential function**

If we write $y = e^x$ and consider x to be a variable, the value of which can change, then for each value given to x, we will generate a corresponding value of y. We would say that y is a function of x and the particular kind of function defined by $y = e^x$ is referred to as the **exponential function**. Another way in which this function is often written is $\exp(x)$. However, in using this notation, it should be kept in mind that $\exp(x)$ means e^x. The form e^x is referred to as 'e to the power of x' and $\exp(x)$ is referred to as 'exponential x'. The variable, x, that appears inside a function is referred to as its **argument**. A form of the exponential function that occurs frequently in chemistry is $y = e^{-x}$ or $y = \exp(-x)$. These functions depend upon x as indicated in Figure 2.1.

The exponential function is important in science because it occurs in the descriptions of a wide variety of phenomena and processes. For example, the curve shown in Figure 2.1(a) appears in simple models that represent the growth of a population of bacteria. The curve in Figure 2.1(b) describes the decline in the number of radioactive nuclei resulting from radioactive decay. In the context of chemistry, this curve describes the fall in concentration of a reactant that is involved in a first order chemical reaction. In these examples, the variable, x, would represent time.

Exponential functions that occur in practice are usually a little more complex than the simple forms e^x and e^{-x}. More general forms of the exponential function are

$$y = A\,e^{ax} \tag{2.17}$$

and

$$y = A\,e^{-ax} \tag{2.18}$$

in which A and a are constants, that is, A and a do not depend upon x, but they may depend upon other things. Plots of these two functions against x

Figure 2.1

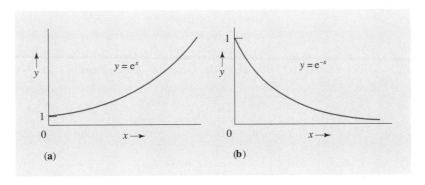

(a)   (b)

have similar shapes to those shown in Figure 2.1. The effect of the constant A is to expand or contract the scale on the vertical axis, or y-axis, whereas the effect of the constant a is to expand or contract the scale on the horizontal axis, or x-axis.

From the description of the general rules governing exponents given in Section 2.2, it is evident that the exponential function has the following properties

$$e^x \times e^y = e^{x+y} \tag{2.19}$$

$$\frac{e^x}{e^y} = e^{x-y} \tag{2.20}$$

$$e^{xy} = (e^x)^y \tag{2.21}$$

$$e^0 = 1 \tag{2.22}$$

Self test questions 2.6

(a) If $e^x = 4$, what is the value of e^{2x}?

(b) If $e^x = 9$, what is the value of $2e^{\frac{x}{2}}$?

(c) If $e^x = 3$ and $e^z = 2$, evaluate (i) e^{x+z}, (ii) e^{x-z}, (iii) e^{2x+z}, (iv) e^{x-2z}

The exponential function and first order chemical reactions

The concentration of a reactant A that is undergoing a first order chemical reaction is related to time according to:

$$[A] = [A]_0 \, e^{-kt} \tag{2.23}$$

in which $[A]_0$ is the initial concentration of A and k is known as the first order rate constant for the reaction. A graph of $[A]$ plotted against time t would have a shape similar to that shown in Figure 2.1(b). After a certain length of time, the concentration of A will have dropped to a half of its initial value. Denoting this period of time by $t_{\frac{1}{2}}$, this means that

$$[A] = \frac{[A]_0}{2} \quad \text{when} \quad t = t_{\frac{1}{2}}$$

Putting these values into equation (2.23) gives

$$\frac{[A]_0}{2} = [A]_0 \exp(-kt_{\frac{1}{2}}) \tag{2.24}$$

Dividing both sides of this equation by $[A]_0$ gives

$$\frac{1}{2} = \exp(-kt_{\frac{1}{2}})$$

and from the definition of a natural logarithm, equation (2.8), we conclude that

$$-kt_{\frac{1}{2}} = \ln(\tfrac{1}{2}) \tag{2.25}$$

Since $\frac{1}{2}$ is the same as 2^{-1}, then $\ln(\tfrac{1}{2}) = \ln(2^{-1})$ and, according to equation (2.10), this is the same as $-\ln 2$. Putting this into equation (2.25) gives $kt_{\frac{1}{2}} = \ln 2$ or

$$t_{\frac{1}{2}} = \frac{\ln 2}{k} \tag{2.26}$$

Equation (2.26) shows that the larger k is, the shorter is the time required for the concentration to drop to half of its initial value. This equation also shows that $t_{\frac{1}{2}}$ does not depend upon the initial concentration $[A]_0$. We could select any time during the course of the reaction and decide to regard it as the time $t = 0$. The time taken for the concentration to drop to a half of what it was initially is the same no matter what initial time is chosen. Figure 2.2 illustrates this for the concentration changes

$$[A]_0 \rightarrow \frac{[A]_0}{2} \qquad \text{and} \qquad \frac{[A]_0}{2} \rightarrow \frac{[A]_0}{4}$$

This characteristic of the exponential curve is useful as a quick method of determining whether a reaction behaves in accordance with first order kinetics. It is not restricted to the fraction $\frac{1}{2}$. For example, if the reaction is a first order reaction, the time taken for the concentration of reactant to fall to 60% of its original value would be the same no matter what original value was taken. In the example below, concentrations of a reactant A at various times are given.

Figure 2.2

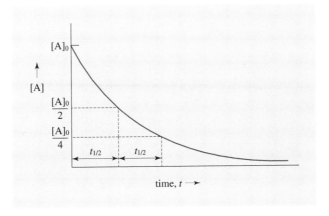

[A]/mol L^{-1}	1×10^{-3}	0.78×10^{-3}	0.61×10^{-3}	0.47×10^{-3}	0.37×10^{-3}
t/seconds	0	5	10	15	20

During the first 5 s, [A] falls from 1×10^{-3} mol L^{-1} to 0.78×10^{-3} mol L^{-1}. Expressed as a percentage of the initial value, the concentration at the end of the first 5 s interval is

$$\frac{0.78 \times 10^{-3}}{1 \times 10^{-3}} \times 100 = 78\%$$

During the next 5 s interval, [A] falls from 0.78×10^{-3} mol L^{-1} to 0.61×10^{-3} mol L^{-1}. Expressed as a percentage of the concentration at the start of this 5 s interval this is

$$\frac{0.61 \times 10^{-3}}{0.78 \times 10^{-3}} \times 100 = 78\%$$

The fact that the concentration of reactant falls by the same percentage over separate 5 s intervals suggests that the reaction behaves in accordance with first order kinetics.

As with the logarithmic function, the argument of the exponential function should not have units or dimensions. In an expression such as

$$[A] = [A]_0 \, e^{-kt}$$

the product kt is dimensionless. If the unit of t is the second, s, then the unit of k should be s^{-1}.

The series expansion of the exponential function

The number e has been stated to be 2.718... and the function e^x has been defined as this number raised to the power of x. However, nothing has been revealed regarding where the number e comes from. There are several ways of defining e, but one of the more useful involves the expansion of the exponential function as the sum of an infinite series of terms, the first five terms of which are shown in equation (2.27):

$$e^x = 1 + x + \frac{x^2}{2!} + \frac{x^3}{3!} + \frac{x^4}{4!} + \cdots \text{etc.}$$
(2.27)

The form of succeeding terms in the series is easily deduced from those written above and the series goes on without end. The numbers 2!, 3!, 4!, and so on, are referred to as 'two factorial', 'three factorial', 'four factorial', and are simply ways of writing down the products $2! = 2 \times 1 = 2$, $3! = 3 \times 2 \times 1 = 6$, $4! = 4 \times 3 \times 2 \times 1 = 24$, etc. The series expansion of e^{-x} is the same but with x replaced by $-x$. The first five terms of this series are

$$e^{-x} = 1 - x + \frac{x^2}{2!} - \frac{x^3}{3!} + \frac{x^4}{4!} - \cdots \text{etc.} \tag{2.28}$$

Before accepting these series expansion as definitions, those who are sceptical would want answers to several questions. The most basic question would be, is it possible that the sum of the infinite series of terms on the right side of equation (2.27) is the same as some number raised to the power x? It is not obvious that this is so but it can be demonstrated to be the case. Also, is this series expansion valid for all values of x? In fact, it is. We could put $x = 1000$ into equation (2.27) and, provided that we add together a sufficient number of terms, the result would approximate to e^{1000}. It might be thought that the sum would become larger and larger the more terms we add and would never approach a finite limit. In fact, this is not the case. For both series, as the number of terms increases, the values of their sums converge on the values e^x and e^{-x} respectively. The notion of convergence is important with regard to infinite series, as such series are of limited use if they do not converge. An example of a series that is not convergent is the harmonic series

$$1 + \frac{1}{2} + \frac{1}{3} + \frac{1}{4} + \frac{1}{5} + \cdots \text{etc.}$$

As more and more terms are added, the sum of terms becomes larger and larger without approaching a finite limit.

We can use equation (2.27) to find a value for e simply by putting $x = 1$. This gives

$$e = 1 + 1 + \frac{1}{2} + \frac{1}{6} + \frac{1}{24} + \frac{1}{120} + \cdots \text{etc.}$$

Adding together just these first six terms gives a value of 2.7177, which is a reasonable approximation to the value of 2.7183. A more accurate value for e could be obtained by adding more terms.

The value of e^x when x is small

In finding a value for e^x using the series expansion, the number of terms required to obtain a result to some specified degree of accuracy reduces the closer the value of x is to zero. For values of x between -1 and $+1$, the terms decline rapidly in value in moving through the series and reasonable approximations can often be found using only the first few terms. For small values of x, use of the first two terms is often sufficient. For example, if $x = 0.1$ the value of e^x to three places of decimals is 1.105. The expansion of e^x using only the first two terms is

$$e^x = 1 + x, \qquad \text{approximately} \tag{2.29}$$

and inserting $x = 0.1$ into this gives $e^x = 1.1$. This result is within 0.5% of the true value and higher accuracy would be expected when x is less than 0.1. The utility of this approach is not in finding approximate numerical values for e^x when x is close to zero, as accurate values can be found easily using a calculator. These approximate forms for e^x are most useful in the derivation of simplified versions of expressions that involve the exponential function. For example, it was mentioned earlier that the concentration of a reactant undergoing a first order chemical reaction depends upon time according to

$$[A] = [A]_0 \, e^{-kt}$$

During the initial stages of the reaction when the product kt is small (less than 0.1), we can expand the exponential function as

$$e^{-kt} = 1 - kt$$

leading to the approximate expression

$$[A] = [A]_0(1 - kt)$$

This shows that in the early stages of the reaction, a plot of concentration $[A]$ against time is almost a straight line. By measuring the gradient of this line, one could obtain an estimate for the value of the rate constant k. Such an approach might be useful in the study of a slow reaction for which k is in the region of $10^{-4} \, \text{s}^{-1}$ and data is collected over a period of about 15 minutes. Throughout the whole of this period, the product kt would be less than 0.1.

| 2.5 | **The binomial series** |

The binomial series is a method of evaluating functions of the type

$$(a + y)^n = a^n \left(1 + \frac{y}{a} \right)^n = a^n (1 + x)^n$$

in which n is non-integral and $x = y/a$. The series expansion of $(1 + x)^n$ is given by

$$(1 + x)^n = 1 + nx + \frac{n(n - 1)}{2!} x^2 + \frac{n(n - 1)(n - 2)}{3!} x^3 + \cdots$$

which converges for $|x| < 1$. ($|x|$ is used to denote the absolute-value of x irrespective of whether it is positive or negative and $|x| < 1$ means that the absolute value should be less than 1.)

This series expansion can be used to obtain approximate values for $(1 + x)^n$ when x is small compared to unity as was done with the exponential series. For small values of x we can write

$$(1 + x)^n = 1 + nx, \qquad \text{approximately}$$

| 2.6 | **Trigonometric functions** |

Trigonometric functions do not appear frequently in chemistry, but they are found in treatments of elementary quantum mechanics and in the description of some experimental techniques such as X-ray diffraction. Introductory courses on quantum mechanics, in particular, often require a knowledge of the properties of sine and cosine functions. These functions are described here for this reason. It is possible that some of the material towards the end of this section could be omitted during the early stages of a chemistry course.

Trigonometric functions are usually defined by reference to a right-angled triangle as shown in Figure 2.3. Usually, angles are measured in degrees, one complete revolution corresponding to 360 degrees (360°). The distinguishing feature of a right-angled triangle is that one of the angles is a right-angle, that is, it has a value of 90°. The sides of such a triangle are named according to their positions in relation to the angle of interest; in this case, the angle α. The side of length o is known as the opposite side, because it is on the opposite side of the triangle to the angle α. The side of length a is adjacent to the angle α and is referred to

Figure 2.3

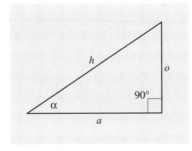

Figure 2.4

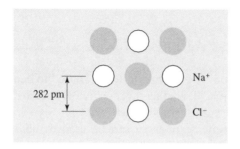

as the adjacent side. The side opposite to the right-angle (90°) is referred to as the hypotenuse and it is the longest side of the triangle. The lengths of the sides of a right-angled triangle are related by the well-known theorem of Pythagoras which asserts that

$$a^2 + o^2 = h^2 \tag{2.30}$$

Self test questions
2.7

The arrangement of sodium and chloride ions in the sodium chloride crystal is as indicated in Figure 2.4. Calculate the distance between the centres of two nearest neighbour sodium ions.

The sine, cosine and tangent functions are defined as the ratios between the sides of a right-angled triangle as follows:

$$\sin \alpha = \frac{o}{h} \tag{2.31}$$

$$\cos \alpha = \frac{a}{h} \tag{2.32}$$

$$\tan \alpha = \frac{o}{a} \tag{2.33}$$

Division of equation (2.31) by equation (2.32) shows that

$$\tan \alpha = \frac{\sin \alpha}{\cos \alpha} \tag{2.34}$$

From these definitions, it is evident that $o = h \sin \alpha$ and $a = h \cos \alpha$.

Substituting these expressions for o and a into equation (2.30) gives

$$h^2(\cos\alpha)^2 + h^2(\sin\alpha)^2 = h^2$$

and dividing both sides of this equation by h^2 gives

$$(\cos\alpha)^2 + (\sin\alpha)^2 = 1 \qquad\qquad (2.35)$$

This is an important relationship between the sine and cosine functions. However, it is a relationship that is generally written down using the notation:

$$\cos^2\alpha + \sin^2\alpha = 1$$

The notation $\cos^2\alpha$ is widely used but it must be remembered that it is intended to denote the more correct $(\cos\alpha)^2$.

In addition to the trigonometric functions referred to above, their inverse functions may also be encountered. The funtion $\sin^{-1}x$ is the angle with a sine equal to x. If $\sin\alpha = x$ then $\alpha = \sin^{-1}x$. The functions $\cos^{-1}x$ and $\tan^{-1}x$ are defined in a similar way. Notice that these functions are multivalued. $\sin^{-1}1$ is the angle α which is such that $\sin\alpha = 1$, and this is true of any angle of the form $(n+\frac{1}{2})\pi$ where n is a positive or negative even integer including zero.

Some particular values of trigonometric functions

Reference to Figure 2.3 indicates that as the angle α decreases in size, a and h become closer in length. In the limit of α becoming zero, a and h would have the same length and, from the definition in equation (2.32), $\cos 0 = 1$. In the same limit of α approaching zero, the length of the opposite side o would approach zero and, from equation (2.31), $\sin 0 = 0$. If we now consider the effects of α becoming larger and approaching $90°$, it is evident that the adjacent side approaches zero and the opposite side of the triangle approaches the length of the hypotenuse h. This leads to the values $\cos 90° = 0$ and $\sin 90° = 1$. When $\alpha = 45°$, o and a are equal in length. From the theorem of Pythagoras, their common length, written here as a, is found from

$$a^2 + a^2 = h^2 \qquad \text{or} \qquad 2a^2 = h^2$$

giving the result

$$a(\text{or }o) = \frac{h}{\sqrt{2}}$$

Figure 2.5

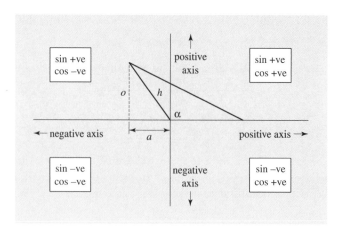

This can now be inserted into equations (2.31) and (2.32) to give

$$\cos 45° = \frac{1}{\sqrt{2}} \quad \text{and} \quad \sin 45° = \frac{1}{\sqrt{2}}$$

Also, since o and a are equal we have $\tan 45° = 1$.

Extension to angles beyond 90° requires us to reconsider how we specify the lengths of the opposite and adjacent sides as indicated in Figure 2.5. In this diagram, the length of the hypotenuse h is considered to be a positive number. However, for an angle between 90° and 180°, o is positive, because it is measured along the positive vertical axis, but a is negative because it is measured along the negative horizontal axis. This means that the sine of the angle α is the ratio of two positive lengths, o and h (see equation 2.31) and is, therefore, itself positive, whereas the cosine of α is the ratio of a negative length to a positive length and so is negative. An angle between 180° and 270° would fall in the third quadrant and both the opposite and adjacent sides of the associated triangle would have negative values. In this quadrant, both sine and cosine functions are negative. The signs of these functions in each of the four quadrants are indicated on the diagram.

Self test questions 2.8

What are the signs, positive or negative, of the following quantities?

(a) $\sin 100°$, (b) $\cos 140°$, (c) $\sin 260°$, (d) $\cos 200°$, (e) $\tan 145°$, (f) $\sin 300°$

Some particular values of the sine and cosine functions are given in Table 2.1.

Table 2.1

Angle, α	$\sin\alpha$	$\cos\alpha$
0	0	1
45°	$\dfrac{1}{\sqrt{2}}$	$\dfrac{1}{\sqrt{2}}$
90°	1	0
135°	$\dfrac{1}{\sqrt{2}}$	$-\dfrac{1}{\sqrt{2}}$
180°	0	−1

The unit of angle

Angles are usually specified in degrees, the size of a degree being determined by the convention that a complete revolution corresponds to a rotation through 360°. However, this is an arbitrary unit of angle. A more fundamental unit is the **radian** which can be defined by reference to Figure 2.6. The size of the angle α is defined as the ratio of the arc length s to the radius r:

$$\alpha = \frac{s}{r}\ \text{radian} \tag{2.36}$$

As the radian is defined as the ratio of two lengths, it is a dimensionless quantity. The correspondence between radians and degrees can be obtained readily by noting that an angle of 360° corresponds to the arc being a complete circle. Since the circumference of a complete circle of radius r is $2\pi r$,

360° is equivalent to $\dfrac{2\pi r}{r}$ radian, or 2π radian.

Figure 2.6

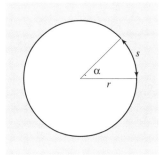

To convert an angle from degrees to radians, we simply divide the angle by 360 to determine the fraction of a complete circle that it represents and multiply by 2π:

$$\text{angle in radians} = \frac{\text{angle in degrees}}{360} \times 2\pi \qquad (2.37)$$

An angle of 1 radian is approximately 57 degrees.

Self test questions 2.9

Express the following angles in radians, writing your answers in terms of π:

(a) 180°, (b) 45°, (c) 135°, (d) 270°, (e) 315°

The oscillatory nature of the sine and cosine functions

Plots of the functions $y = \sin x$ and $y = \cos x$ are shown in Figure 2.7. In this figure, the scales on the horizontal x-axes are marked in radians and, although only the positive portions of the x-axes are shown, the curves continue along the negative portions. Both functions are oscillatory, that is, they undulate up and down. They are also **periodic**, that is, the same value of the function is repeated at regular intervals of 2π along the x-axis. This fact is expressed by the relationships $\sin x = \sin(x + 2\pi)$ and $\cos x = \cos(x + 2\pi)$. It is evident that the plots of the sine and cosine functions have similar shapes but that the sine function is displaced to the right relative to the cosine function by an amount $\pi/2$. This is

Figure 2.7

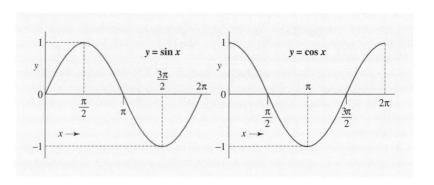

expressed by

$$\cos x = \sin\left(x + \frac{\pi}{2}\right)$$

The two functions also have different symmetry properties. The cosine function is symmetric about the vertical y-axis so that $\cos(-x) = \cos x$, and it is said to be an **even function** of x. The sine function is anti-symmetric, since $\sin(-x) = -\sin x$, and is said to be an **odd function** of x.

Self test questions
2.10

If x is such that $\sin x = 0.4$, determine the values of

(a) $\sin(-x)$, (b) $\sin(x + 2\pi)$, (c) $\sin(x + \pi)$, (d) $\sin(x - \pi)$

More general forms of these functions are often written as

$$y = A \sin ax \qquad \text{and} \qquad y = A \cos ax \tag{2.38}$$

in which A and a are constants. The constant A is referred to as the **amplitude**. The functions written in equation (2.38) oscillate between maximum and minimum values of $+A$ and $-A$. The constant a extends or compresses the scale on the horizontal axis. For example, if a is equal to 3, then the argument of the sine (or cosine) function is $3x$, not x. The sine and cosine curves then execute one complete cycle when x changes so that $3x$ varies from 0 to 2π. If x is a length, this implies that one complete cycle is executed as x increases from 0 to $2\pi/3$ and this quantity would be referred to as the **wavelength** of the function. Wavelength is usually denoted by λ (lambda) and, in the general case, λ is given by

$$\lambda = \frac{2\pi}{a}$$

or

$$a = \frac{2\pi}{\lambda} \tag{2.39}$$

The quantity denoted by a in equation (2.39) is often referred to as the wavevector and is written as k.

When x denotes distance, the constant a is related to wavelength as shown in equation (2.39) and the general forms of the sine and cosine functions can be written as

$$y = A \sin\left(\frac{2\pi}{\lambda}x\right) \qquad \text{and} \qquad y = A \cos\left(\frac{2\pi}{\lambda}x\right) \tag{2.40}$$

Figure 2.8

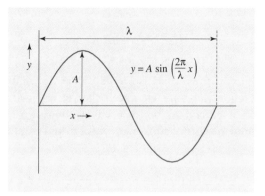

Determine the amplitudes and wavelengths of the waves described by the following functions:

(a) $2\sin(0.5x)$, (b) $0.1\cos(8x)$, (c) $10\sin(4\pi x)$, (d) $8\cos(\pi x)$

Sine and cosine functions in the time domain

In the case discussed above, the variable x was considered to be a length and the sine and cosine functions could describe, for example, the profile of a wave on the surface of water at a particular time. It is also possible to use these functions to describe the way in which a quantity oscillates in time. In this case, we would simply replace the variable x, denoting distance, with the variable t, denoting time. The general forms of the functions could be written as $y = A\sin at$ and $y = A\cos at$. The **period** of an oscillation is the time taken to execute one complete cycle. The period is usually denoted by T. As time increases from 0 to T, the argument at changes from 0 to 2π, that is, $aT = 2\pi$ or

$$a = \frac{2\pi}{T}$$

The time-dependent sine and cosine functions can now be written as

$$y = A\sin\left(\frac{2\pi}{T}t\right) \qquad \text{and} \qquad y = A\cos\left(\frac{2\pi}{T}t\right) \qquad (2.41)$$

If a quantity undergoes one complete cycle of oscillation in a time of 0.1 s, then it oscillates at a rate of 10 cycles per second. The number of cycles executed per unit time is the **frequency** of oscillation and it is related to the period of oscillation by

$$\text{frequency} = \frac{1}{T}$$

Frequency is often denoted by the symbol ν (nu). If time is specified in seconds, then frequency is specified in s^{-1}, a unit which is given the name hertz, or Hz. The expressions given in equation (2.41) can be simplified by defining an **angular frequency** by

$$\text{angular frequency} = \frac{2\pi}{T}$$

Angular frequency is denoted by the symbol ω (omega). Using this notation, we can write the sine and cosine functions in the time domain as

$$y = A \sin \omega t \qquad \text{and} \qquad y = A \cos \omega t \qquad (2.42)$$

in which the angular frequency, ω, is related to the frequency, ν, by $\omega = 2\pi\nu$.

**Self test questions
2.12**

Determine the frequencies and angular frequencies of the following functions:

(a) $10 \sin(100t)$, (b) $8 \sin(0.01t)$, (c) $10 \cos(0.05t)$, (d) $5 \cos(10^5 t)$

Series expansions for the sine and cosine functions

In this chapter, the exponential function and the simple trigonometric functions have been discussed, and it might appear that the exponential function has little in common with the sine and cosine functions. Certainly, the graphs shown in Figures 2.1 and 2.7 do not suggest any similarity. However, both the sine and cosine functions can be expanded as infinite series, and these series have features that are also found in the series expansion of the exponential function. If x is expressed *in radians*, the sine and cosine functions can be written in the forms:

$$\sin x = x - \frac{x^3}{3!} + \frac{x^5}{5!} - \frac{x^7}{7!} + \cdots \text{etc.} \qquad (2.43)$$

$$\cos x = 1 - \frac{x^2}{2!} + \frac{x^4}{4!} - \frac{x^6}{6!} + \cdots \text{etc.} \qquad (2.44)$$

Comparing these with the series expansion of the exponential function, some clear similarities emerge:

$$e^x = 1 + x + \frac{x^2}{2!} + \frac{x^3}{3!} + \frac{x^4}{4!} + \cdots \text{etc.}$$

All three series contain similar terms, but the sine series contains only terms in odd powers of x and the cosine series contains only terms in even powers of x. These facts are reflected in the symmetry properties of the trigonometric functions. $\sin x$ is an odd function as shown by $\sin(-x) = -\sin x$, and $\cos x$ is an even function: $\cos(-x) = \cos x$. As with the exponential series, the series expansions of $\sin x$ and $\cos x$ can be used to find approximate values for these functions when x is small and *expressed in radians*:

$$\sin x \approx x \quad \text{and} \quad \cos x \approx 1 - x \quad \text{for small values of } x \quad (2.45)$$

(The symbol '$\approx$' means 'is approximately equal to'.)

The similarities between the exponential series and the series for the trigonometric functions suggests that these apparently different functions should be related in some way. These functions are related, but the relationship cannot be established without introducing another type of number known as an **imaginary number**. The unit imaginary number is denoted by i and its defining property is

$$i = \sqrt{-1} \tag{2.46}$$

or

$$i^2 = -1$$

None of the real numbers with which we are familiar have this property. For example,

$$(+1) \times (+1) = +1 \quad \text{and} \quad (-1) \times (-1) = +1.$$

Other properties of the number i that follow from its definition are:

$$i^3 = i^2 \times i = (-1) \times i, \quad \text{or simply} \quad -i$$

$$i^4 = i^2 \times i^2 = (-1) \times (-1) = +1$$

$$i^5 = i^4 \times i = i, \ldots \text{etc.}$$

A number written as, for example 3i, is also imaginary and is simply three times as large as the number i. This number has the property

$$(3i)^2 = -9$$

These properties of the imaginary numbers allow us to write out the series expansion for the function e^{ix}

$$e^{ix} = 1 + (ix) + \frac{(ix)^2}{2!} + \frac{(ix)^3}{3!} + \frac{(ix)^4}{4!} + \frac{(ix)^5}{5!} + \cdots \text{etc.}$$

$$= 1 + ix - \frac{x^2}{2!} - i\frac{x^3}{3!} + \frac{x^4}{4!} + i\frac{x^5}{5!} - \cdots \text{etc.} \tag{2.47}$$

Inspection of this expansion reveals that it is the sum of the series expansion for $\cos x$ and the series expansion for $\sin x$ multiplied by i:

$$e^{ix} = \cos x + i \sin x \tag{2.48}$$

Bearing in mind that the number i is not a real number, and the size of anything that we can measure is always expressed as a real number, one may wonder about the usefulness of this expression. However, it is much more amenable to mathematical manipulation than are the sine and cosine functions. As a simple example of this it is noted that $e^{ix}.e^{iy} = e^{i(x+y)}$, but there are no similarly simple expressions for products such as $(\sin x).(\sin y)$.

More generally, we can write

$$e^{iax} = \cos ax + i \sin ax \tag{2.49}$$

in which a is a constant. As $\cos ax$ and $\sin ax$ are periodic functions, e^{iax} is also periodic and can be used in the description of oscillatory phenomena. Replacing x by $-x$ in equation (2.49) gives the relationship

$$e^{-iax} = \cos ax - i \sin ax \tag{2.50}$$

Adding equations (2.49) and (2.50) gives

$$\cos ax = \frac{e^{iax} + e^{-iax}}{2}$$

and subtracting equation (2.50) from equation (2.49) gives

$$\sin ax = \frac{e^{iax} - e^{iax}}{2i}$$

To conclude this brief summary of the connection between the exponential and trigonometric functions, it is noted that there is also an intriguing connection between the irrational numbers, e and π, and the imaginary number i that is revealed by putting x equal to π in equation (2.48):

$$e^{i\pi} = -1$$

Answers to self test questions

2.1 (a) 5, (b) -7, (c) -3, (d) -1

2.2 (a) 1.3, (b) 0.6, (c) 1.7, (d) 1.4, (e) -1.7

2.3 (a) 8, (b) 3, (c) 2.7, (d) 2.4

2.4 (a) $10^{-5}\,\text{mol}\,\text{L}^{-1}$, (b) Solution A contains the higher concentration of hydrogen ions

2.5 $-20\,895\,\text{J}\,\text{mol}^{-1}$ or $-20.895\,\text{kJ}\,\text{mol}^{-1}$

2.6 (a) 16, (b) 6, (c) (i) 6, (ii) 1.5, (iii) 18, (iv) 0.75

2.7 399 pm

2.8 (a) $+$, (b) $-$, (c) $-$, (d) $-$, (e) $-$, (f) $-$

2.9 (a) π, (b) $\dfrac{\pi}{4}$, (c) $\dfrac{3\pi}{4}$, (d) $\dfrac{3\pi}{2}$, (e) $\dfrac{7\pi}{4}$

2.10 (a) -0.4, (b) 0.4, (c) -0.4, (d) -0.4

2.11 (a) 2, 4π, (b) 0.1, $\dfrac{\pi}{4}$, (c) 10, 0.5, (d) 8, 2

2.12 (a) $\dfrac{50}{\pi}$, 100, (b) $\dfrac{1}{200\pi}$, 0.01, (c) $\dfrac{1}{40\pi}$, 0.05, (d) $\dfrac{5 \times 10^4}{\pi}$, 1×10^5

Questions on Chapter 2

2.1 Calculate the values of x that satisfy the following equations:

(a) $10^x = 4$, (b) $10^x = 0.5$, (c) $10^{2x} = 9 \times 10^{-4}$, (d) $10^{-x} = 0.25$, (e) $10^{-2x} = 0.25$

2.2 If $\log_{10} a = 3$ and $\log_{10} b = 4.5$, determine the values of:

(a) $\log_{10} ab$, (b) $\log_{10} \left(\dfrac{b}{a}\right)$, (c) $\log_{10} \left(\dfrac{1}{ab}\right)$, (d) $\log_{10} a^2$,

(e) $\log_{10} a^2 b$, (f) $\log_{10} \sqrt{(ab)}$

2.3 Solutions A, B and C have hydrogen ion concentrations of $4.5 \times 10^{-3} \, \text{mol L}^{-1}$, $4.6 \times 10^{-3} \, \text{mol L}^{-1}$ and $4.7 \times 10^{-3} \, \text{mol L}^{-1}$ respectively. Calculate the pH values of these solutions. To how many significant figures would pH have to be measured in order to distinguish between solutions B and C?

2.4 Calculate the *changes* in the pH of a solution that result from the following changes in concentration, indicating whether the change in pH is an increase or decrease:

(a) $[H^+]$ is doubled, (b) $[H^+]$ is halved, (c) $[H^+]$ is multiplied by 10,
(d) $[OH^-]$ is multiplied by 5, (e) $[OH^-]$ is divided by 4,
(f) $[H^+]$ is changed to $[H^+]^2$.

(In answering (d) and (e), assume that $[H^+][OH^-] = 1 \times 10^{-14}$.)

2.5 Suppose that we decide to define a quantity to be denoted by Ph as

$$\text{Ph} = \log_{10} \left(\frac{[H^+]}{[H^+]_0}\right),$$

in which the standard concentration, $[H^+]_0$, has the value $1 \times 10^{-7} \, \text{mol L}^{-1}$. What values of Ph correspond to the following values of pH (a) 3, (b) 5, (c) 7, (d) 9, (e) 11?

2.6 The intensity of light transmitted through a light-absorbing solution at a particular wavelength is given by the equation

$$I_t = I_0 10^{-\varepsilon c l}$$

in which I_t is the intensity of the transmitted light, I_0 the intensity of the light that is incident on the solution, ε is the molar absorptivity of the solution, c is its concentration and l is the length of the light path through the solution. If, for a solution of a dye, I_t is one tenth of I_0 when the concentration of dye is $2 \times 10^{-5} \, \text{mol L}^{-1}$ and l is 1 cm, calculate the value of ε in units of $\text{mol}^{-1} \, \text{L cm}^{-1}$.

2.7 If $e^{-x} = 0.25$, calculate the values of

(a) e^x, (b) e^{2x}, (c) $\sqrt{(e^{-2x})}$, (d) $e^{\frac{x}{2}}$.

2.8 If $\ln p = 0.2$ and $\ln q = -0.1$, calculate the values of

(a) $\ln p^2$, (b) $\ln pq$, (c) $\ln pq^2$, (d) $\ln \left(\dfrac{p}{q}\right)$, (e) $\ln \sqrt{p}$

2.9   The equilibrium constant K_p for the gas phase equilibrium

$$2NO_2 \rightleftharpoons N_2O_4$$

is related to the change in Gibbs free energy, ΔG^0, for the reaction by

$$\Delta G^0 = -RT \ln K_p.$$

If the value of ΔG^0 (at 298 K) for this reaction is $-4.73\,\text{kJ}\,\text{mol}^{-1}$, calculate the value of K_p at 298 K. (Note that $R = 8.314\,\text{J}\,\text{K}^{-1}\,\text{mol}^{-1}$. When ΔG^0 is used in conjunction with this value for R, care must be taken to ensure that the units of ΔG^0 are compatible with those of R.)

2.10 In a chemical reaction in solution that behaves in accordance with first order kinetics, the concentration of reactant A falls exponentially from its initial value of $5 \times 10^{-3}\,\text{mol}\,\text{L}^{-1}$ to $3 \times 10^{-3}\,\text{mol}\,\text{L}^{-1}$ in a time of 20 s. What would you expect the concentration of A to be (a) after 40 s and (b) after 60 s?

2.11 The pressure of the atmosphere, at uniform temperature, depends upon height above sea level according to the barometric equation which can be written as

$$p = p_0\,e^{-ah}$$

in which p is the pressure at height h, and p_0 is the pressure at sea level. For air, the constant α is approximately equal to $6 \times 10^{-5}\,\text{m}^{-1}$ at 298 K.

(a) Calculate the height above sea level at which the pressure of the atmosphere is $0.9p_0$.
(b) What would be the pressure at twice this height?

2.12 The disintegration of radioactive nuclei is described by the equation

$$N = N_0\,e^{-\lambda t}$$

in which N_0 is the number of nuclei at $t = 0$, N is the number remaining after time t and λ is the decay constant. The half-life is defined as the time taken for the number of nuclei to decay from N_0 to a half of this value. The half-life of ^{106}Rh is 30 s. What is the value of λ for ^{106}Rh?

2.13 A quantity P is defined by the equation

$$P = \frac{e^{ax} - e^{-ax}}{a}$$

Estimate the value of P when the product ax is less than 0.1 and x is equal to 5.

Figure 2.9

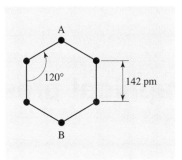

2.14 The carbon atoms in graphite are arranged in layers and, in any layer, they are located in a regular hexagonal array as indicated in Figure 2.9. Calculate the distance between the atoms labelled A and B.

2.15 Convert the following angles from radians to degrees:

(a) $\dfrac{\pi}{6}$, (b) $\dfrac{\pi}{4}$, (c) $\dfrac{2\pi}{3}$, (d) $\dfrac{2\pi}{5}$, (e) $\dfrac{\pi}{10}$, (f) $\dfrac{2\pi}{15}$

2.16 (a) Write down in radians four values of x for which $\sin x = 0$.
(b) Write down in radians four values of x for which $\cos x = 0$.
(c) Write down in radians three values of x for which $\sin x = \cos x$
(d) Write down a *general expression* for the values of x for which $\sin x = 0$.

2.17 By reference to Table 2.1, find values of the function $\sin x + \cos x$ for values of x between 0 and 2π radians at intervals of $\pi/4$ (45°). Sketch a graph indicating how this function varies with x in the above range, noting how the resulting graph differs from that of $\sin x$.

2.18 What are the wavelengths of waves described by the following functions?

(a) $\sin x$, (b) $\sin \pi x$, (c) $\sin\left(\dfrac{x}{10}\right)$, (d) $\cos 4x$, (e) $8\cos\left(\dfrac{\pi x}{8}\right)$

2.19 What are the frequencies of waves described by the following functions?

(a) $2\sin(4\pi t)$, (b) $\cos(10\pi t)$, (c) $\sin(100t)$, (d) $5\sin(0.1t)$,

(e) $\cos\left(\dfrac{\pi t}{4}\right)$

2.20 Write down approximate expressions for the following when x is small and expressed in radians:

(a) $\dfrac{\sin x}{x}$, (b) $\dfrac{\cos x}{x}$, (c) $\sin(x + 2\pi)$, (d) $\dfrac{\sin(x + \pi)}{x}$

3 The graphical presentation of data

The simplest type of graph is the straight line plot, examples of which are shown in Figure 3.1. Graphs illustrate how a variable y changes as another variable x is changed. They can be considered to consist of a number of points that join up to give the line displayed. The position of a point on a graph is specified by its **coordinates**. Coordinates are the values of x and y that locate the point and they are written as (x, y). As an example, the point with an x value equal to 10 and a y value equal to 5 is shown in Figure 3.1(a) as having coordinates $(10, 5)$. The construction of a graph involves plotting many such points to establish the shape of the line that illustrates how y depends upon x. The **origin** of the graph is the point at which both x and y have the value 0 and it is denoted by $(0, 0)$.

Figure 3.1

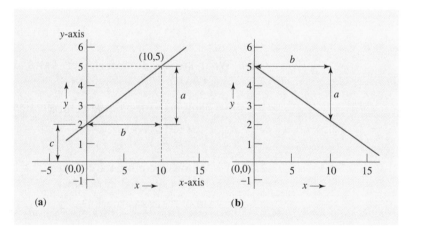

(a)   (b)

The **gradient** of a straight line graph is a measure of the steepness of slope of the plotted line. The line in Figure 3.1(a) has a gradient given by

$$\text{gradient} = \frac{a}{b} = \frac{(5-2)}{10} = 0.3$$

In this case, the gradient is a positive quantity because as x increases, y also increases. In Figure 3.1(b), y decreases as x increases and the distance a should be regarded as a negative quantity making the gradient negative. A horizontal straight line has a gradient equal to 0.

The **intercept** on the y-axis is the value of y at which the plotted straight line intersects the y-axis *when the y-axis is drawn through the point $x = 0$ on the x-axis*. In Figure 3.1(a), the value of the intercept is 2 and it is denoted by c. Sometimes, it is desirable to construct a graph in which the axes do not intersect at the origin $(0, 0)$. In this case it must be borne in mind that if the y-axis does not pass through the point $x = 0$ on the x-axis, the point at which the plotted line cuts the y-axis will not be the intercept.

Self test questions 3.1

Some of the following points have the property that they all lie on a line that is parallel to the x-axis. Identify the points with this property.

$$(-1, 1), (0, 2), (0, 1), (1, 3), (1, 1), (2, -2), (2, 0), (3, 1), (-1, -1)$$

Dependent and independent variables

The vertical axis, or y-axis, is conventionally used to denote values of a **dependent variable** and the horizontal axis, or x-axis, denotes the corresponding values of the **independent variable**. For example, in displaying how a concentration changes with time, concentration would be regarded as the dependent variable because its value depends upon time, which would be regarded as the independent variable. Concentration values would then be represented as distances along the y-axis and times would be represented as distances along the x-axis. Sometimes it is difficult to decide which variable should be described as independent and which as dependent. The volume of a fixed amount of a gas at constant temperature could be said to depend upon the pressure of the gas. Alternatively, we could say that, under the same conditions, the pressure depends on the volume. However, if an experiment involved systematically changing the volume and recording the resulting changes in pressure, we would regard pressure as the dependent variable and plot it along the y-axis.

3.2 | **The equation that represents a straight line**

The straight lines shown in Figure 3.1(a) and (b) can be represented by equations which enable one to calculate the value of y for any value of x. To find out what the equation is for the line in Figure 3.1(a), we note that when x is zero, y has the value 2. Also, when x increases by 10 units, y increases by 3 units, or an increase in x of 1 unit produces an increase in y of 0.3. These observations are embodied in the equation

$$y = 0.3x + 2$$

When x is put equal to zero, y has the value 2, and for each unit increase in x, the increase in y is 0.3 as required. In general, the equation that represents a straight line has the form

$$y = mx + c \tag{3.1}$$

in which m is the gradient of the line obtained by plotting y against x, and c is the intercept on the y-axis. A relationship of this form is referred to as a **linear** relationship and y is said to depend linearly upon x. In terms of the quantities shown in Figure 3.1,

$$m = \frac{a}{b} \tag{3.2}$$

It is important to note that the constant m that appears in equation (3.1) can be identified with the gradient of a plotted line only when y is plotted on the vertical axis and x is plotted on the horizontal axis. Plotting x along the vertical axis and y along the horizontal axis would give a line with gradient m^{-1}.

Self test questions
3.2

Plot a graph of y against x using the data given below and determine the values of m and c in the equation $y = mx + c$.

x	0.5	1.0	1.5	2.0	2.5
y	0.60	0.70	0.80	0.90	1.00

Scales on axes

The axes of a graph should be marked at regular intervals with numbers indicating the size of the quantities plotted. For example, in a particular case, it might be necessary to plot concentrations along an axis and

Figure 3.2

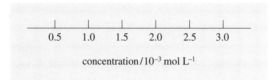

these concentrations could have values such as 0.6×10^{-3}, 1.1×10^{-3}, 1.5×10^{-3}, 2.0×10^{-3} and 2.6×10^{-3}, all in units of $mol\,L^{-1}$. A suitable scale could have divisions marked at 0.5, 1.0, 1.5, 2.0, 2.5 and 3.0 and the axis would be labelled 'concentration$/10^{-3}\,mol\,L^{-1}$'. This would be read as 'concentration in units of $10^{-3}\,mol\,L^{-1}$. The appearance of such a scale is shown in Figure 3.2.

Often the quantities to be plotted have values that make it undesirable to include the origin, $(0,0)$, on the graph. For example, this would be the case if all the values to be plotted on the y-axis fell within a range such as 8 to 12 and all the values to be plotted on the x-axis were in a range such as 30 to 40. In such a case, it is usually preferable to choose scales that encompass only the limited range of values to be plotted and to omit the origin. This is illustrated in Figure 3.3, in which the data points that are confined to the upper right corner in graph (a) have been plotted on axes with expanded scales in graph (b). Measurements of the intercept and gradient could be made on graph (b) with improved accuracy. However, the intersection of the plotted line and the vertical axis at $y = 8.8$ on graph (b) is no longer the true intercept because the origin of the graph has been shifted to the point $(30, 8)$. The value of the true intercept is somewhere between 2 and 4 as shown in Figure 3.3(a). This value can be found by measuring the gradient of the plotted line from graph (b) and using this in conjunction with equation (3.1) to determine the value of c.

Let us suppose that the measured value of the gradient is 0.2. From graph (b), it is evident that when x has the value 30, y is equal to 8.8.

Figure 3.3

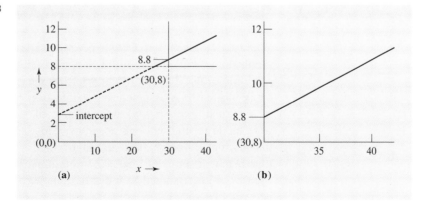

Putting these values into the equation $y = mx + c$ gives

$$8.8 = 0.2 \times 30 + c$$

which is readily solved for c with the result $c = 2.8$.

A straight line graph is drawn using vertical and horizontal axes that cross at the point $(6, 0)$. The plotted line cuts the vertical axis at the point $y = 17$ and it has gradient equal to 2. Calculate the value of c in the equation $y = mx + c$ that describes the line.

The units of the gradient and intercept

In general, both the intercept and the gradient of a straight line graph have units that are determined by the units used to specify the quantities plotted on the vertical and horizontal axes. For example, if a concentration in units of $mol\,L^{-1}$ is plotted on the vertical axis, and time specified in seconds is recorded on the horizontal axis, the intercept will have units of $mol\,L^{-1}$ and the gradient will be a concentration divided by a time with units of $mol\,L^{-1}\,s^{-1}$.

The volume of a gas is measured under conditions of constant pressure and it is plotted against the temperature of the gas. If volume is measured in litres and temperature in kelvin, what are the units of the gradient of the graph?

3.3   Real graphs and scatter

When a graph is plotted from experimental data, it is often found that the points do not fall on a smooth line or curve but instead display a degree of random scatter. This scatter arises from measurement errors in the data being plotted. It is assumed that whatever is being measured would vary in a regular manner without evidence of scatter if the measurements were made to high enough accuracy. This being the case, it is incorrect to construct a 'stock market' graph in which adjacent points are connected together by a series of lines. The points marked on the graph shown in Figure 3.4 are assumed to indicate that there exists a linear relationship between the variable, y, and the variable, x. The drawn line represents

Figure 3.4

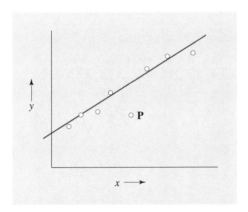

a reasonable guess at what the line would look like in the absence of scatter. This line is drawn so that, as far as can be judged, the points are evenly distributed on either side of it. Other lines that are reasonable fits to the data, but with slightly different intercepts and gradients, could be drawn and these could be used to estimate the maximum expected errors in the gradient and intercept of the plot.

The point P shown in Figure 3.4 is a 'bad data' point. It is clear that it does not fit in with the trend exhibited by the other points and this suggests that the measurement that gave rise to this point was defective in some way. Bad data points are not included in an analysis of data but, rather than simply ignore them, it would be better to repeat the measurements from which they were derived. One of the advantages of the graphical representation of data is that it allows such points to be easily recognised and, if the graph is plotted when measurements are being taken, it gives early warning that something is going wrong.

The least squares method

The method described above of fitting a straight line to a set of points with scatter is subjective in that different people confronted with the same task would be expected to draw slightly different lines. The least squares method overcomes this problem by specifying a procedure for finding a line that is as good a fit to the data as can be expected. The line derived by this method should not be considered to be the 'true' line; it is merely the best that can be done subject to the limited accuracy inherent in the data. In Figure 3.5, four points are shown scattered about a line which is a candidate for the best fit to the plotted data. The vertical distances between the data points and the line are denoted by s_1, s_2, s_3

Figure 3.5

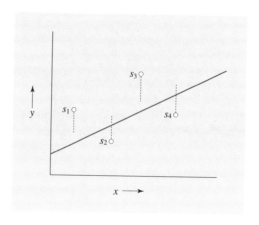

and s_4. These quantities are sometimes referred to as **residuals**. We now consider the sum of squares

$$S = s_1^2 + s_2^2 + s_3^2 + s_4^2$$

The sum has been written down for only four points but it could be extended to include any number of points. As this is a sum of quantities squared, it will always be positive no matter what the distances s_1, s_2, s_3 and s_4 are. In Figure 3.5, s_2 and s_4 are negative because they are displacements below the line, but their squares are still positive numbers. The least squares method is based on the premise that the line of best fit, also called the **line of regression,** is the one for which the value of the sum S is a minimum. This sum will be a minimum when the line is drawn so that points are evenly distributed about it as with the line in Figure 3.5. It might be thought that finding a line that satisfies this criterion would be a lengthy process. However, it can be shown that the gradient and intercept of the required line are given by quite simple formulae. However, before stating these formulae it is necessary to consider a notation that simplifies writing out sums of many similar terms. We denote the x and y coordinates of the data points by x_i and y_i where the label i is used to specify which point is being referred to. For the first point (the one corresponding to the smallest value of x), i is 1. If there are N points in total, then the values of i run from 1 to N. Sums are written out using the notation exemplified below:

$$\sum_{i=1}^{N} x_i = x_1 + x_2 + x_3 + \cdots + x_N$$

The symbol $\sum$ (sigma) indicates that the various x_i are to be added starting with x_1 and ending with x_N. The lower limit to the range is indicated by the $i = 1$ below the sign and the upper limit is indicated by the N above it.

Similarly,

$$\sum_{i=1}^{N} x_i y_i = x_1 y_1 + x_2 y_2 + \cdots + x_N y_N$$

and

$$\sum_{i=1}^{N} x_i^2 = x_1^2 + x_2^2 + \cdots + x_N^2$$

The values for these sums are easily calculated from the coordinates of the data points but, for large values of N, this is a job that would usually be done using a computer program. Using this notation, the gradient m and intercept c of the line of best fit are

$$m = \frac{N \sum_{i=1}^{N} x_i y_i - \sum_{i=1}^{N} x_i \sum_{i=1}^{N} y_i}{N \sum_{i=1}^{N} x_i^2 - \left(\sum_{i=1}^{N} x_i \right)^2} \qquad (3.3)$$

and

$$c = \frac{\sum_{i=1}^{N} x_i^2 \sum_{i=1}^{N} y_i - \sum_{i=1}^{N} x_i \sum_{i=1}^{N} x_i y_i}{N \sum_{i=1}^{N} x_i^2 - \left(\sum_{i=1}^{N} x_i \right)^2} \qquad (3.4)$$

These formulae may appear complex but they have the simple forms,

$$m = \frac{NS_3 - S_1 S_2}{NS_4 - S_1^2} \qquad \text{and} \qquad c = \frac{S_4 S_2 - S_1 S_3}{NS_4 - S_1^2}$$

where the definitions of the summations S_1, S_2, S_3 and S_4 are found by comparison with equations (3.3) and (3.4). Once these sums have been evaluated, it is a simple matter to calculate m and c.

With the aid of a computer program to evaluate the sums in equations (3.3) and (3.4), the least squares method of finding m and c is simple to apply. However, some caution should be exercised before accepting the results of these calculations. An uncritical application of the least squares method would include bad data points, such as the point P shown in Figure 3.4, and this would have an adverse effect on the accuracy of the calculated values for m and c. Also, it is not necessarily the case that the extent of error is the same for all data points. For practical reasons, some data points may be more difficult to measure accurately than others and these will have a disproportionate effect on the accuracy of the end result. Features such as these are more easily appreciated when points are plotted than they are when numbers are keyed into a computer, and graphs, whether computer generated or hand-drawn, remain an important aid in the interpretation of data.

Writing equations in linear form

In order to obtain a straight line when a variable, y, is plotted against another variable, x, it is necessary that y and x are related by an equation of the form

$$y = mx + c$$

in which m and c do not depend on x. Often, equations that do not have this form can be manipulated so that they can be used to obtain straight line plots. A form of equation that is often manipulated in this way is exemplified by equation (2.23) that was discussed in Chapter 2. This equation relates to first order chemical kinetics and it describes how the concentration, [A], of a reactant depends upon the initial concentration, $[A]_0$, and time:

$$[A] = [A]_0 e^{-kt}$$

As discussed in Chapter 2, a plot of [A] against time gives an exponential curve. However, by taking natural logarithms of both sides of this equation we obtain

$$\ln [A] = \ln [A]_0 + \ln(e^{-kt}) = \ln [A]_0 - kt$$

This equation has the form of $y = mx + c$ provided that we identify $\ln[A]$ with y and identify t with x. A graph of $\ln[A]$ against t would be a straight line with gradient equal to $-k$ and intercept equal to $\ln[A]_0$ as shown in Figure 3.6.

This graph has a negative gradient that is equal to $-k$. In a particular case, the gradient could be, for example, $-2.5 \times 10^{-2}\,\text{s}^{-1}$. Equating this to $-k$ ensures that k has the *positive* value of $2.5 \times 10^{-2}\,\text{s}^{-1}$. The value of the gradient does not depend upon the units of concentration. Since,

$$\frac{[A]}{[A]_0} = e^{-kt}$$

and the value of the ratio $[A]/[A]_0$ is independent of the units used to specify concentration, k is also independent of those units. We could regard this ratio as the ratio of two pure numbers such as

$$\frac{22.4 \times 10^{-3}}{50 \times 10^{-3}} \qquad \text{instead of} \qquad \frac{22.4 \times 10^{-3}\,\text{mol L}^{-1}}{50 \times 10^{-3}\,\text{mol L}^{-1}}$$

Figure 3.6

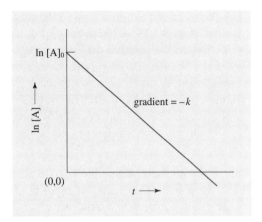

In the quantity ln[A], [A] should be regarded as such a pure number rather than a number with units attached. This avoids the inconsistency of considering ln[A] to be dimensionless, as required, when [A] has units of concentration.

Self test questions
3.5

If $[A] = [A]_0 e^{-kt}$, what would be the gradient of the line obtained by plotting $\ln([A]_0/[A])$ against t?

In the context of chemistry, there are several frequently encountered relationships of the form

$$y = y_0 e^{ax}$$

in which a does not depend upon x. These equations can always be written in the form

$$\ln y = \ln y_0 + ax$$

allowing a straight line graph to be constructed by plotting $\ln y$ against x. An example is the Arrhenius equation which shows how a rate constant, k, depends upon the absolute temperature, T. This equation can be written as

$$k = A e^{-E_a/RT}$$

in which A is called the pre-exponential factor, E_a is known as the activation energy, T is the temperature in kelvin and R is the gas constant. By taking natural logarithms of both sides of this equation we obtain

$$\ln k = \ln A - \frac{E_a}{RT}$$

This has the form of $y = mx + c$ provided that we identify $\ln k$ with y and $1/T$ with x. A plot of $\ln k$ against $1/T$ then gives a straight line with a gradient equal to $-E_a/R$ and an intercept equal to $\ln A$.

Self test questions

3.6

Variables y and x are related by the equation $y = A e^{-ax^2}$. What quantities could be plotted in order to obtain a straight line graph which would allow the constant a to be found from the gradient?

Many equations are amenable to representation as linear plots but the ways in which they must be manipulated to allow this are very varied. In some cases, it is simply a matter of identifying the variables to be plotted in an appropriate way. For example, second order reactions of the type,

$$A + A \longrightarrow \text{product}$$

are described by the equation

$$\frac{1}{[A]} = \frac{1}{[A]_0} + kt$$

in which k is a second order rate constant, $[A]_0$ is the initial concentration of A and $[A]$ is the concentration at time t. A straight line graph can be constructed in this case by identifying $1/[A]$ with y and t with x in the equation $y = mx + c$. The gradient of the line would be equal to k and the intercept on the y-axis would be $1/[A]_0$. In other cases, an equation may have to be rearranged to identify variables that are linearly related. For example, the adsorption of a gas on the surface of a solid at constant temperature can be described by an equation known as the Langmuir adsorption isotherm

$$V = \frac{V_c ap}{(1 + ap)}$$

in which a is a constant, V_c is the volume of gas required to completely cover the surface of the solid with a layer one molecule thick, and V is the volume of gas that is actually adsorbed on the surface when the pressure is p. The two related variables in this equation are V and p but the connection between them is not linear. Multiplying both sides of the equation by $(1 + ap)$ gives

$$(1 + ap)V = V_c ap$$

Dividing this by $V V_c a$ gives

$$\frac{p}{V} = \frac{p}{V_c} + \frac{1}{aV_c}$$

In this form of the equation, we can identify two variables that are linearly related. These are p/V and p. A graph of p/V plotted against p would be a straight line with a gradient equal to $1/V_c$ and an intercept on the vertical axis equal to $1/aV_c$. Measurement of the gradient and intercept from such a graph would enable both a and $V - c$ to be determined.

Self test questions 3.7

The variable y is related to the variable x by the equation,

$$y = \frac{ax + b}{x}$$

in which a and b are constants, the values of which are to be found. What quantity could y be plotted against in order to obtain a straight line graph from which a and b could be found?

3.5   Finding the values of exponents in empirical relationships

It sometimes happens that there is reason to believe that some quantity y is related to another, x, by an empirical equation of the form

$$y = ax^n$$

in which a is a constant and n is an exponent, the value of which is uncertain or unknown. An empirical relationship is one that is suggested by experiment rather than derived from an application of theory. One way of finding out the value of n is to take logarithms of this equation and to plot the logarithm of y against the logarithm of x. Either logarithms to the base 10 or natural logarithms could be used. Here, we will take logarithms to the base 10:

$$\log_{10} y = \log_{10} a + n \log_{10} x$$

It can be seen that this equation is of the form $y = mx + c$ if we identify $\log_{10} y$ with y and $\log_{10} x$ with x. The straight line obtained by plotting $\log_{10} y$ against $\log_{10} x$ would have a gradient equal to n thus allowing n to be determined. This method can be used to determine the order of a chemical reaction from measurements of the initial rate of reaction. In a reaction

$$A + B \longrightarrow \text{products}$$

the rate of reaction, which can be defined as the fall in concentration of A per second, is expected to be given by some relationship of the form

$$\text{rate} = k[A]^m[B]^n$$

in which k is a rate constant and m and n are the orders of reaction with respect to A and B. We expect m and n to have values such as 1 or 2. The initial rate of reaction is amenable to measurement and it is related to the known initial concentrations $[A]_0$ and $[B]_0$ by

$$\text{initial rate} = k[A]_0^m[B]_0^n$$

Taking logarithms of this equation, we obtain

$$\log_{10}(\text{initial rate}) = \log_{10}k + m\log_{10}[A]_0 + n\log_{10}[B]_0$$

By measuring the initial rate for different values of $[A]_0$ with $[B]_0$ fixed, it is possible to determine the value of m from the gradient of a graph of $\log_{10}(\text{initial rate})$ against $\log_{10}[A]_0$. Similarly, by measuring the initial rate with $[A]_0$ fixed but for different values of $[B]_0$ and plotting the appropriate graph, n could be determined.

Self test questions 3.8

The acid catalysed bromination of acetone can be represented by

$$CH_3COCH_3 + Br_2 \xrightarrow{\ H^+\ } CH_3COCH_2Br + H^+ + Br^-$$

The rate of reaction of bromine is monitored and assumed to be related to the concentrations of reactants by

$$\text{rate} = k[CH_3COCH_3]^m[Br_2]^n[H^+]^p$$

What measurements could be made and what graphs could be plotted to determine the values of m and p?

Answers to self test questions

3.1 The points $(-1, 1)$, $(0, 1)$, $(1, 1)$ and $(3, 1)$ lie on the line $y = 1$

3.2 The gradient is 0.2 and the intercept is 0.5

3.3 $c = 5$

3.4 $L\,K^{-1}$

3.5 The gradient is k

3.6 Plot $\ln y$ against x^2. The gradient of the line is equal to $-a$

3.7 Plot y against $1/x$. The gradient is equal to b and the intercept is equal to a

3.8 Measure the initial rate of reaction for various concentrations of acetone keeping the concentrations of bromine and H^+ fixed. Plot a graph of $\log_{10}$(initial rate) against $\log_{10}[CH_3COCH_3]$. The gradient of this plot is equal to m. To find p, measure the initial rate keeping the concentrations of acetone and bromine fixed at different concentrations of H^+. Plot a graph of $\log_{10}$(initial rate) against $\log_{10}[H^+]$. The gradient of the plot is equal to p.

Questions on Chapter 3

3.1 Three of the following points lie on the same line that has a gradient equal to 1:

$$(-2, 2),\ (0, 1),\ (2, 3),\ (0, 3),\ (1, 1),\ (0, -1),\ (1, 2).$$

Identify the three points.

3.2 The points in group (a) lie on a straight line, and the points in group (b) lie on another straight line. Determine the gradients of these two lines.

(a) $(-4, 0),\ (-2, 1),\ (0, 2)$ (b) $(0, 3),\ (1, 0),\ (2, -3)$

3.3 The y-axis of a graph passes through the point $x = 10^{-3}$ on the x-axis. If a plotted straight line crosses the y-axis at $y = 0.2$ and the gradient of the line is 250, what is the value of c in the equation, $y = mx + c$?

   If the gradient of the line had been -100, what would have been the value of c?

3.4 In each of the following cases, the variable y is related to the variable x as indicated by the equation given and a and b are constants. In each case, state the function of x against which y should be plotted in order to produce a straight line graph:

(a) $y = a + bx^2$
(b) $y = a - b \ln x$
(c) $y = a + \dfrac{b}{x^2}$
(d) $xy = a$

3.5 The variable y is related to the variable x by the equation

$$\frac{1}{y} = \sqrt{\frac{x + a}{x}}$$

in which a is a constant. What quantities could be plotted so as give a straight line graph from which the value of a could be obtained?

3.6 The variables x and y are related by the following equation:

$$y = \frac{ax + b}{x}$$

Some values of x and y are given below

x	0.05	0.1	0.2	0.4
y	7	6	5.5	5.25

By plotting a suitable graph, determine the values of the constants a and b.

3.7 In the course of a first order chemical reaction of the type

A $\longrightarrow$ product

the concentration of the reactant A decreases with time as indicated below

$A/\text{mmol L}^{-1}$	1.00	0.90	0.82	0.74	0.67	0.61
Time /s	0	2	4	6	8	10

By plotting a suitable straight line graph, determine the value of the rate constant for the reaction.

3.8 The rate constant k for a first order chemical reaction varies with temperature as indicated below:

k/s^{-1}	0.134	0.430	1.28	3.57	9.38	23.3
T/K	300	310	320	330	340	350

Assuming that the reaction behaves in accordance with the Arrhenius equation, plot a suitable graph to determine the value of the activation energy.

4 The elements of algebra

If we dissolve $10\,g$ of sodium chloride in $100\,g$ of water, the mass of the resulting solution would be $110\,g$. The way in which this simple calculation is done can be made general by writing it as an algebraic formula

$$\text{mass of solution, } M = M_{\text{NaCl}} + M_{\text{water}}$$

in which M_{NaCl} is the mass of sodium chloride and M_{water} is the mass of water. This formula is true for any mass of sodium chloride and any mass of water within the limits imposed by the solubility of sodium chloride in water. The right-hand side of the equation is a very simple example of an **algebraic expression**. One of the advantages of algebraic expressions is that they are more general than the arithmetic operations that they represent.

If both M_{NaCl} and M_{water} are specified in grams and we wish to convert all masses to milligrams then we simply multiply each mass by 1000:

$$\text{mass of solution in milligrams} = 1000 M_{\text{NaCl}} + 1000 M_{\text{water}}$$

4.1 Brackets

The above expression would normally be written as $1000(M_{\text{NaCl}} + M_{\text{water}})$, the number 1000 outside the brackets multiplying each of the terms within. Brackets can be used to enclose sums or differences of *quantities of the same type*. In this example, the two terms within the brackets are both masses. In general

$$a(b + c) = ab + ac \qquad \text{and} \qquad a(b - c) = ab - ac$$

or more generally

$$a(b + c + d + \cdots) = ab + ac + ad + \cdots$$

As a trivial extension of this, division of a bracketed quantity amounts to division of each term contained within it:

$$\frac{1}{a}(b + c + d + \cdots) = \frac{b}{a} + \frac{c}{a} + \frac{d}{a} + \cdots$$

For example,

$$\frac{(4a + 2b - c)}{2} = 2a + b - \frac{c}{2}$$

In multiplying out brackets it is often necessary to bear in mind that a product such as $(-a) \times (-a)$ is $+a^2$, and that, for example, $-2 \times (-b) = +2b$ and $-2a \times (-2b) = +4ab$.

Self test questions
4.1

Write out the following expressions as a series of terms with the brackets removed:

(a) $5(a - b)$, (b) $2(3a + b)$, (c) $a(2a + b)$, (d) $3a(2b + c)$,

(e) $2b(a - b^2)$, (f) $2a^2(a + 2b)$, (g) $2a(a + 2b - c)$, (h) $-a(b - 2c)$

(i) $\dfrac{(3a + b)}{3}$, (j) $\dfrac{(ab + b)}{b}$, (k) $\dfrac{(a + b)}{ab}$, (l) $\dfrac{(a^2 + b^2)}{ab}$

In some cases, it is desirable to write a sum of terms as a product by inserting brackets. For example, the quantity $a^2 + ab$ consists of two terms, a^2 and ab, both of which have the factor a in common. We can write this sum as

$$a^2 + ab = a(a + b)$$

Some other examples are

(a) $a^2 + a^3 b = a^2(1 + ab)$

(b) $\dfrac{1}{a} + \dfrac{1}{ab} = \dfrac{1}{a}\left(1 + \dfrac{1}{b}\right)$

(c) $\sqrt{a} + \dfrac{1}{\sqrt{a}} = \sqrt{a}\left(1 + \dfrac{1}{a}\right)$,   note that $a = \sqrt{a} \times \sqrt{a}$

so that

$$\sqrt{a}\left(1 + \dfrac{1}{a}\right) = \sqrt{a} + \dfrac{\sqrt{a}}{a} = \sqrt{a} + \dfrac{\sqrt{a}}{\sqrt{a}\sqrt{a}} = \sqrt{a} + \dfrac{1}{\sqrt{a}}$$

(d) $a + b = a\left(1 + \dfrac{b}{a}\right)$

(e) $1 + e^{2x} = e^x(e^{-x} + e^x)$

In each case, the validity of these equations can be demonstrated by multiplying out the products shown on the right-hand side.

Self test questions
4.2

Determine the algebraic expressions that should be written inside the brackets shown below

(a) $2a^2 + ab = 2a(\ldots)$, (b) $a + b = ab(\ldots)$, (c) $\dfrac{1}{ab} - \dfrac{1}{b^2} = \dfrac{1}{b}(\ldots)$

(d) $\sqrt{a} + a = \sqrt{a}(\ldots)$, (e) $ae^x + be^{2x} = e^x(\ldots)$,

(f) $e^{x+a} - e^{x-a} = e^x(\ldots)$

4.2   **Products of bracketed terms**

The product $(a + b)(c + d)$ can be written out in either of the following ways:

$$(a + b)(c + d) = (a + b)c + (a + b)d$$

or

$$(a + b)(c + d) = a(c + d) + b(c + d)$$

In the first case, each term in the second bracket has been multiplied by $(a + b)$ and in the second case, each term in the first bracket has been multiplied by $(c + d)$. The two expressions on the right of these equations are the same and after removing all brackets, are seen to be $ac + bc + ad + bd$. Some special cases of products of bracketed quantities are the following:

$$(a + b)^2 = (a + b)(a + b) = a^2 + 2ab + b^2$$
$$(a - b)^2 = (a - b)(a - b) = a^2 - 2ab + b^2$$
$$(a + b)(a - b) = a^2 - b^2$$

In multiplying out brackets it is usual to collect together similar terms in the result. For example $(2a + 3)(a - 1)$ can be written as

$$(2a + 3)(a - 1) = 2a^2 - 2a + 3a - 3$$

but the terms $-2a$ and $+3a$ would be combined to give $+a$ and the result would be written as $2a^2 + a - 3$.

Multiply out the following brackets

(a) $(2 + x)(x + 1)$, (b) $(2x + 1)(x + 2)$, (c) $(x + 2)(x - 1)$,
(d) $(3x - 1)(2x + 1)$, (e) $(x - 2)(x - 1)$, (f) $(2x - 1)(1 - x)$,
(g) $(2x - 1)(2 - 2x)$, (h) $(x + 2)(x - 2)$

4.3 | **Algebraic fractions**

An algebraic fraction has the form

$$\text{algebraic fraction} = \frac{y}{x}$$

in which x and y are variables. The rules for adding, subtracting, multiplying and dividing algebraic fractions are simply more general versions of the rules used for arithmetic fractions described in Chapter 1. To add two algebraic fractions, we must first find a common denominator. For the fractions $1/x$ and $1/y$, a common denominator can always be found by multiplying together x and y, so that

$$\frac{1}{x} = \frac{y}{xy} \quad \text{and} \quad \frac{1}{y} = \frac{x}{xy}$$

This enables us to write

$$\frac{1}{x} + \frac{1}{y} = \frac{y}{xy} + \frac{x}{xy} = \frac{(y + x)}{xy}$$

As with arithmetic fractions, a quick way of arriving at the result is to employ the cross multiplication procedure illustrated below

$$\frac{1}{x} \quad \underset{\longleftrightarrow}{\overset{+}{\times}} \quad \frac{1}{y} = \frac{y + x}{xy}$$

For example,

$$\frac{1}{2x} + \frac{1}{3y} = \frac{3y + 2x}{6xy}$$

Subtracting algebraic fractions is done in a similar way with the minus sign replacing the plus sign.

Carry out the following additions or subtractions

(a) $\dfrac{1}{x} + \dfrac{1}{2y}$, (b) $\dfrac{1}{2x} + \dfrac{2}{y}$, (c) $\dfrac{x}{y} + \dfrac{y}{x}$, (d) $\dfrac{1}{x} - \dfrac{x}{y}$, (e) $\dfrac{3}{x} - \dfrac{1}{2y}$, (f) $\dfrac{1}{xy} - \dfrac{2}{x^2}$

The multiplication of algebraic fractions is adequately illustrated by the following examples

(a) $\dfrac{1}{x} \times \dfrac{1}{y} = \dfrac{1}{xy}$

(b) $\dfrac{2}{3x} \times \dfrac{x}{2y} = \dfrac{2x}{6xy} = \dfrac{1}{3y}$

The denominators and numerators of each fraction are simply multiplied together as indicated. Division by an algebraic fraction x/y is equivalent to multiplication by the fraction y/x. For example,

$$\frac{3}{x} \bigg/ \frac{2x}{3y} = \frac{3}{x} \times \frac{3y}{2x} = \frac{9y}{2x^2}$$

4.4   **Equations**

An equation has the form $a = b$, and it signifies that the quantities a and b have the same value. When a and b have physical dimensions, they must have the same dimensions. An important feature of equations is that if the same operation is carried out on the quantities on both sides of the equation, the equation remains true. For example, for an equation of the form

$$x - a = b$$

we can add a to both sides to give

$$x - a + a = b + a \qquad \text{or} \qquad x = b + a$$

This leads to the general rule that if we move a term from one side of an equation to the other, we change its sign. If $x + a = b$, then $x = b - a$.

Similarly, with an equation of the form $ax = b$, we can divide both sides by a to give

$$\frac{ax}{a} = \frac{b}{a} \qquad \text{or} \qquad x = \frac{b}{a}$$

The net result is that we have moved the factor a from the left side of the equation to the right side but it has been moved diagonally so that b becomes divided by a. For an equation of the form

$$\frac{x}{a} = b$$

we can multiply both sides by a to give

$$\frac{x}{a} \times a = ba \qquad \text{or} \qquad x = ba$$

Again, the quantity a has been moved across from left to right but it has been moved diagonally so that it multiplies b.

To find an expression for the quantity x in an equation such as $ax + b = c$ it is necessary to rewrite it so that any terms containing x appear on one side of the equation and all terms not containing x appear on the other side. This can be done by moving b from the left side to the right side:

$$ax = c - b$$

We can now divide both sides by a to give

$$x = \frac{c - b}{a}$$

Note that $ax + b = c$ is quite different from $x(a + b) = c$ as in this second example, x is a factor of the left side of the equation. In this case, we can find an expression for x simply by dividing both sides of the equation by $(a + b)$:

$$x = \frac{c}{(a + b)}$$

To determine an expression for x in an equation such as $ax + b = cx + d$ it is again necessary to move all terms containing x to one side of the equation and all other terms to the other side:

$$ax - cx = d - b$$
$$x(a - c) = d - b$$
$$x = \frac{(d - b)}{(a - c)}$$

The validity of the results of these manipulations rests on the underlying principle that if we do the same thing to both sides of an equation, the resulting relationship remains true.

**Self test questions
4.5**

Find the value for x in each of the following expressions:

(a) $x + 3 = 5$, (b) $3x = 12$, (c) $2x + 3 = 7$, (d) $2(x + 3) = 8$,

(e) $\frac{x}{3} = 4$, (f) $\frac{x + 3}{2} = 4$, (g) $\frac{2x - 3}{7} = 1$, (h) $2x + 3 = x + 5$,

(i) $2(x + 3) = x + 5$, (j) $\frac{3x + 2}{2} = x + 5$

| 4.5 | **Equations containing functions** |

Often, equations encountered in chemistry contain functions such as those described in Chapter 2. For example, an electrochemical cell that is used to measure the concentration of an ionic species X in solution could have a cell potential, E, given by an equation such as

$$E = E_0 - \frac{RT}{nF}\ln[X]$$

in which E_0 is the standard cell potential, R is the gas constant, T is the temperature in kelvin, n is the number of electrons involved in the electron transfer process and F is the Faraday constant. To obtain an expression for the concentration [X], it is first necessary to rearrange the equation so that the function alone appears on one side of the equation and all other variables and constants appear on the other side. In this case, this rearrangement would be done as follows:

$$\frac{RT}{nF}\ln[X] = E_0 - E$$

$$\ln[X] = \frac{nF}{RT}(E_0 - E)$$

The function can now be *inverted* to obtain an expression for [X]:

$$[X] = \exp\left\{\frac{nF}{RT}(E_0 - E)\right\}$$

(Note that if $\ln x = a$, then $x = e^a$ which is the same as $\exp(a)$.) The procedure illustrated here is generally applicable when it is required to find an expression for a quantity contained within a function. The first step is to rearrange the equation containing the function so that the function alone appears on one side. The function is then inverted to obtain an expression for the quantity of interest.

| 4.6 | **Expressions within the square root sign** |

It is quite common to find that the solution to a problem emerges as an expression contained within the square root sign. An example of an expression of this sort is $\sqrt{a^2b}$. The root sign, $\sqrt{}$, is best considered to be an instruction to find the quantity which when multiplied by itself, or squared, gives the result a^2b. The expression $\sqrt{a^2b}$ is the same as $\sqrt{a^2} \times \sqrt{b}$ which can be written as $\pm a\sqrt{b}$. The symbol $\pm$ (plus or minus) arises because both $(+a)^2$ and $(-a)^2$ are equal to a^2. Other related examples are given below:

$$\sqrt{a^2 + a^2 b} = \pm a \sqrt{1 + b}$$

$$\sqrt{a^3 + a^2 b} = \pm a \sqrt{a + b}$$

$$a\sqrt{b + \frac{c}{a^2}} = \sqrt{a^2 b + c}$$

| 4.7 | **Quadratic equations** |

The general quadratic equation in x has the form

$$ax^2 + bx + c = 0$$

in which a, b and c do not depend upon x. The essential feature of a quadratic equation in x is that it contains a term in x^2. An example is the equation $x^2 - 3x + 2 = 0$ in which a is equal to 1, b is -3 and c is equal to 2. This equation is true for two values of x which are $x = 2$ and $x = 1$. In general, quadratic equations are satisfied by two values of x; they are said to have two **solutions**. When quadratic equations occur in the analysis of practical problems, both solutions can have physical interpretations in some cases but in others, one of the solutions might not correspond to a physically possible condition and would be discarded. The two solutions for the quadratic equation given above are found from

$$x = \frac{-b \pm \sqrt{b^2 - 4ac}}{2a}$$

in which the $\pm$ sign is used to indicate that one solution is obtained by using the $+$ sign and the other is obtained by using the $-$ sign. The two values of x that satisfy a quadratic equation are often referred to as its **roots**.

**Self test questions
4.6**

Find the roots of the following quadratic equations:

(a) $x^2 - 5x + 6 = 0$, (b) $x^2 - x - 2 = 0$, (c) $2x^2 - 8x + 6 = 0$, (d) $x^2 - 2x = 0$

The essential feature of a quadratic equation in x is that it contains a term in x^2, but this may not be immediately obvious. For example, the equation

$$x - 4 + \frac{3}{x} = 0$$

does not contain a term in x^2 explicitly, but if we multiply both sides of the equation by x we obtain

$$x^2 - 4x + 3 = 0$$

which has the two solutions $x = 3$ and $x = 1$.

4.8	**Equations in several variables**

An equation such as $2x + y = 4$ cannot be solved to find *unique* values of x and y. For any value of y that we chose, it is possible to find a corresponding value for x from the rearranged equation

$$x = \frac{4 - y}{2}$$

In order to find unique values for x and y, it is necessary to have some other equation connecting them that is independent of the first. For example, unique values of x and y can be found that satisfy the two equations

$$2x + y = 4$$

and

$$x + 2y = 5$$

A standard procedure to enable one to find out what these values of x and y are involves arranging that each equation contains a common term. In this case, multiplying every term in the first equation by 2 ensures that both equations contain the term $2y$. Alternatively, we could multiply each term in the second equation by 2 and both equations would then contain the term $2x$. Adopting the first strategy gives

$$4x + 2y = 8$$
$$x + 2y = 5$$

If we now subtract each term in the second equation from the corresponding term in the first equation we obtain

$$3x = 3, \qquad \text{which has the solution } x = 1$$

By inserting this value for x into either equation, we can determine the corresponding value for y. For example, inserting it into the second equation gives

$$1 + 2y = 5 \quad \text{or} \quad 2y = 4$$

which is true when $y = 2$.

Independent equations such as $2x + y = 4$ and $x + 2y = 5$ are referred to as **simultaneous equations**. To determine the values of two quantities, x and y, it is necessary to have two independent relationships between them. To determine unique values of three quantities, x, y and z, we must have three independent relationships between them. For example, the equations

$$x + y + z = 2$$

$$2x + y - z = 5$$

$$x + y + 2z = 1$$

are satisfied by the unique values $x = 1$, $y = 2$, and $z = -1$. These values can be found by an extension of the method applied to two simultaneous equations. For example, by subtracting each term in the last equation from the corresponding term in the first we obtain

$$-z = 1 \quad \text{or} \quad z = -1$$

Putting this value for z into the first and second equations gives

$$x + y = 3$$

and

$$2x + y = 4$$

which can then be solved to give $x = 1$ and $y = 2$.

**Self test questions
4.7**

Find values of x and y that satisfy the following equations:

(a) $2x - y = 2$ and $x + y = 4$, (b) $2x + y = 5$ and $4x - y = 1$,
(c) $2x + y = 1$ and $3x + 2y = 1$

The simultaneous equations considered above are described as **linear** equations in x and y. If we were to find pairs of values of x and y that satisfy the equation $2x + y = 5$, for example, and then plot these values as points on a graph, the points would fall on a straight line. That this is so is made evident by rearranging the equation in the form $y = -2x + 5$, which is the equation for a straight line with gradient equal to -2. However, the technique used to find the values of two quantities that are related by two independent equations is not restricted to equations in which the variables of interest are linearly related. For example, the two equations $\ln x + 2y = 3$ and $2\ln x + y = 2$ could be solved to find values for $\ln x$ and y. Solving these two equations for $\ln x$ and y would reveal that $\ln x = 1/3$, so that $x = \exp(1/3) = 1.396$.

| 4.9 | **Partial fractions** |

Partial fractions are encountered in the analysis of the rate equations governing second order reactions of the type:

$$A + B \longrightarrow \text{product}$$

The details of their occurrence will not be dealt with at this stage. It suffices to indicate that the problem amounts to writing a fraction such as

$$\frac{1}{(a-x)(b-x)}$$

in which a and b are constants (they are initial concentrations of the species A and B in the application referred to), in the form of two separate partial fractions

$$\frac{P}{(a-x)} + \frac{Q}{(b-x)}$$

in which P and Q are constants to be determined. We can rewrite this second form as (see Section 4.3)

$$\frac{P(b-x) + Q(a-x)}{(a-x)(b-x)}$$

showing that this is the same as the original fraction provided that

$$P(b-x) + Q(a-x) = 1$$

Multiplying out the brackets and collecting together terms in x gives

$$Pb + Qa - (P+Q)x = 1$$

It is evident that the left side of this equation contains a term in the variable x whereas the right side doesn't, indicating that the left side should not depend upon x. This suggests that the quantity $P+Q$ should be equal to zero and $Pb + Qa$ should be equal to 1.

$$P + Q = 0$$
$$Pb + Qa = 1$$

From these two simultaneous equations, we can find the values of P and Q when we know the values of a and b. For example, if $a = 1$ and $b = 2$, we have

$$P + Q = 0 \quad \text{or} \quad P = -Q$$

and

$$2P + Q = 1$$

It is readily shown that these two equations are satisfied when $P = 1$ and $Q = -1$ giving the result

$$\frac{1}{(1-x)(2-x)} = \frac{1}{(1-x)} - \frac{1}{(2-x)}$$

Self test questions 4.8

Write out the following expressions as a sum of partial fractions

(a) $\dfrac{1}{(2-x)(3-x)}$, (b) $\dfrac{1}{(1-x)(2-x)}$, (c) $\dfrac{2}{(1-x)(2-x)}$

4.10 | **Imaginary and complex numbers**

It was noted in Chapter 2 that the unit imaginary number i has the defining property

$$i \times i = -1$$

and that this property is not shared by any number in the set of real numbers with which we are familiar. The number 3i is also imaginary and has the property

$$3i \times 3i = -9$$

Other examples of multiplication of imaginary numbers are

$$4i \times 3i = -12$$

$$(-4i) \times 3i = 12$$

$$(-4i) \times (-3i) = -12$$

The reciprocal of the unit imaginary number, $1/i$, is readily obtained by noting that

$$\frac{1}{i} = \frac{-(-1)}{i} = \frac{-i^2}{i} = -i$$

so that

$$\frac{2}{3i} = -\frac{2i}{3}$$

**Self test questions
4.9**

Evaluate the following products

(a) $2i \times 2i$, (b) $2i \times (-3i)$, (c) $4i \times (2i)^2$, (d) $(-5i) \times (-3i)$

A complex number is a number with a real and an imaginary part. An example of such a number is $2 + 3i$ in which the real part is 2 and the imaginary part is $3i$. The general form of a complex number is $a + ib$ in which a and b are real numbers. It is not necessary to use complex numbers in the description of measurable physical properties such as volume, energy or temperature, all of which can be adequately represented by the set of real numbers. In the study of chemistry and chemical sciences, imaginary and complex numbers rarely appear. However, they do arise in quantum theory which is used to describe the properties and behaviour of small systems such as atoms and molecules. It is for this reason that a brief account of the algebra of imaginary and complex numbers is given here.

Addition and subtraction of complex numbers

In adding or subtracting two complex numbers, we simple add or subtract the real and imaginary parts independently. For example,

$$(3 + 2i) + (2 + 4i) = 5 + 6i$$

and

$$(3 + 2i) - (2 + 4i) = 1 - 2i$$

Multiplication of complex numbers and complex conjugates

Complex numbers are multiplied in the same way as any two bracketed quantities (see Section 4.2). For example,

$$(2 + 3i)(4 + 5i) = 8 + 12i + 10i + 15i^2$$
$$= 8 + 22i - 15$$
$$= -7 + 22i$$

The result of multiplication is generally to give another complex number. However, this is not the case when a complex number is multiplied by its **complex conjugate**. The complex conjugate of a complex number is obtained by reversing the sign before the imaginary part so that, for example, the complex conjugate of the number $2 + 3i$ is $2 - 3i$. If we denote the complex number $2 + 3i$ by Z then the complex conjugate, $2 - 3i$, would be denoted by Z^*. Multiplying the complex number by its complex conjugate gives

$$ZZ^* = (2 + 3i)(2 - 3i)$$

$$= 4 + 6i - 6i - 9i^2$$

$$= 4 + 9 = 13$$

The result is a positive real number. It is easily shown that for any complex number $Z = a + ib$,

$$ZZ^* = (a + ib)(a - ib)$$

$$= a^2 + b^2$$

and this result will always be real and positive. The significance of this result emerges when we ask how large a particular complex number is. As a complex number consists of two parts, the answer to the question isn't obvious. For example, is the number $1 + 3i$ larger or smaller than the number $2 + 2i$? A meaning can be attached to this question if we represent the numbers in graphical form on what is known as an **Argand diagram**. On this type of diagram, the imaginary part of the number is plotted along the vertical, or imaginary, axis and the real part is plotted along the horizontal axis. A complex number $a + ib$ is represented by a line from the origin to the point (a, b). It can be seen that the number $1 + 3i$ is represented by a line that is longer than that representing the number $2 + 2i$. From the theorem of Pythagoras, the lengths of these lines are $\sqrt{1^2 + 3^2}$ and $\sqrt{2^2 + 2^2}$ respectively. In general, the length of the line or vector representing the complex number $Z = (a + ib)$ is $\sqrt{a^2 + b^2}$ or $\sqrt{ZZ^*}$. The positive quantity $\sqrt{ZZ^*}$ is

Figure 4.1

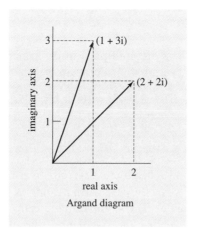

Argand diagram

known as the **modulus** of the complex number Z and it can be regarded as a measure of the size of the number.

Evaluate the following products:

(a) $(1+i)(3+2i)$, (b) $(2-3i)(1+2i)$, (c) $(2+i)(1+2i)$, (d) $(1+i)(1-i)$

Write down the complex conjugates of the following complex numbers:

(e) $(4-3i)$, (f) $(2+i)$, (g) e^{ix}

Complex numbers and quadratic equations

Imaginary and complex numbers can appear as the solutions of quadratic equations and also as solutions to equations in higher powers of x. For example, the equation $x^2 + 3 = 0$ can be rearranged to

$$x^2 = -3$$

so that

$$x = \pm\sqrt{-3} = \pm 3i$$

The general solutions to the quadratic equation $ax^2 + bx + c = 0$,

$$x = \frac{-b \pm \sqrt{b^2 - 4ac}}{2a}$$

will be complex whenever the constants a, b and c are such that $4ac > b^2$. This is the case for the quadratic equation $x^2 - 2x + 2 = 0$ which has roots

$$x = \frac{2 \pm \sqrt{4-8}}{2}$$

$$x = 1 + i \qquad \text{or} \qquad x = 1 - i$$

Answers   **to self test questions**

4.1   (a) $5a - 5b$, (b) $6a + 2b$, (c) $2a^2 + ab$, (d) $6ab + 3ac$, (e) $2ba - 2b^3$,

(f) $2a^3 + 4a^2b$, (g) $2a^2 + 4ab - 2ac$, (h) $-ab + 2ac$, (i) $a + \dfrac{b}{3}$,

(j) $a + 1$, (k) $\dfrac{1}{b} + \dfrac{1}{a}$, (l) $\dfrac{a}{b} + \dfrac{b}{a}$

4.2 (a) $a + \dfrac{b}{2}$, (b) $\dfrac{1}{b} + \dfrac{1}{a}$, (c) $\dfrac{1}{a} - \dfrac{1}{b}$, (d) $1 + \sqrt{a}$, (e) $a + b\,e^x$, (f) $e^a - e^{-a}$

4.3 (a) $x^2 + 3x + 2$, (b) $2x^2 + 5x + 2$, (c) $x^2 + x - 2$, (d) $6x^2 + x - 1$,
(e) $x^2 - 3x + 2$, (f) $-2x^2 + 3x - 1$, (g) $-4x^2 + 6x - 2$, (h) $x^2 - 4$

4.4 (a) $\dfrac{2y + x}{2xy}$, (b) $\dfrac{y + 4x}{2xy}$, (c) $\dfrac{x^2 + y^2}{xy}$, (d) $\dfrac{y - x^2}{xy}$,
(e) $\dfrac{6y - x}{2xy}$, (f) $\dfrac{x^2 - 2xy}{x^3 y}$

4.5 (a) 2, (b) 4, (c) 2, (d) 1, (e) 12, (f) 5, (g) 5, (h) 2, (i) -1, (j) 8

4.6 (a) 2, 3, (b) -1, 2, (c) 1, 3, (d) 0, 2

4.7 (a) $x = 2$, $y = 2$, (b) $x = 1$, $y = 3$, (c) $x = 1$, $y = -1$

4.8 (a) $\dfrac{1}{(2 - x)} - \dfrac{1}{(3 - x)}$, (b) $\dfrac{1}{(1 - x)} - \dfrac{1}{(2 - x)}$, (c) $\dfrac{2}{(1 - x)} - \dfrac{2}{(2 - x)}$

4.9 (a) -4, (b) 6, (c) -16i, (d) -15

4.10 (a) $1 + 5$i, (b) $8 + $i, (c) 5i, (d) 2, (e) $4 + 3$i, (f) $2 - $i, (g) e^{-ix}

Questions **on Chapter 4**

4.1 Write down the expression that should appear in the brackets shown:

(a) $x\,e^x + x^2 = x(\ldots)$, (b) $e^{2x} + x\,e^x = e^x(\ldots)$, (c) $x^2 + a = x(\ldots)$,
(d) $(x + x\,e^x)^2 = x^2(\ldots)^2$

4.2 Multiply out the following brackets:

(a) $(3x + 2)(2x + 1)$, (b) $(2x - 1)(x + 1)$, (c) $(x - 2)(2 - x)$,
(d) $(2 + e^x)(1 + e^{-x})$, (e) $(1 + x^2)(1 - x)$, (f) $(1 + 2x)(1 - e^x)$

4.3 Rearrange the following equations so as to give expressions for the variable x:

(a) $a = (b + x)c$, (b) $a = (b + x) + c$, (c) $a = (b + x)c + dx$

4.4 The change in Gibbs free energy, ΔG, for a chemical reaction is related to the change in enthalpy, ΔH, and the change in entropy, ΔS, by the equation

$$\Delta G = \Delta H - T\Delta S$$

in which T is the temperature in Kelvin. For the complete combustion of glucose at 298 K, $\Delta G = -2880\,\text{kJ}\,\text{mol}^{-1}$ and $\Delta H = -2800\,\text{kJ}\,\text{mol}^{-1}$.

(a) Rearrange the above equation to obtain an expression for ΔS.

(b) Calculate the value of ΔS.

4.5 Add or subtract the following algebraic fractions as indicated and simplify the resulting expressions as appropriate:

(a) $\dfrac{a}{x} + \dfrac{a}{3x}$, (b) $\dfrac{a}{2x} - \dfrac{b}{x}$, (c) $\dfrac{1-x}{x} - \dfrac{x}{1-x}$, (d) $\dfrac{1}{(1+x)} - \dfrac{1}{(1+x)^2}$

4.6 Rearrange the following equations so as to obtain expressions for the variable x:

(a) $a = b + cx^2$, (b) $a = b + c\,e^x$, (c) $a = b + c\,e^{3x}$,

(d) $a = b + c\ln 2x$

4.7 The equilibrium constant K for a reaction at equilibrium is related to the change in standard Gibbs free energy of the reaction, ΔG^0, by the relationship

$$\Delta G^0 = -RT\ln K$$

in which R is the gas constant and T is the temperature in kelvin.

(a) Write down an expression for K showing how it depends upon ΔG^0. The change in standard Gibbs free energy, ΔG^0, is related to the change in standard enthalpy, ΔH^0, and the change in standard *entropy*, ΔS^0, by the relationship

$$\Delta G^0 = \Delta H^0 - T\Delta S^0$$

(b) Write down an expression showing how K depends upon ΔH^0 and ΔS^0.

(c) If the value of the equilibrium constant at temperature T_1 is K_1 and its value at temperature T_2 is K_2, derive an expression for the ratio K_1/K_2 assuming that the values of ΔH^0 and ΔS^0 do not change when the temperature changes.

4.8 The hydrogen ion concentration in a solution of a weak acid with an acid dissociation constant equal to K_a is given by the approximate relationship

$$[\mathrm{H}^+] = \sqrt{K_a c}$$

in which c is the concentration of the weak acid. Assuming that K_a does not change with the concentration of the acid, by what factor must the concentration be increased in order to increase the value of $[\mathrm{H}^+]$ by a factor of 1.5? What difference would such a change make to the pH of the solution?

4.9   Find the values of x that satisfy the following equations:

(a) $x^2 - 2.5x + 1 = 0$, (b) $x^2 - 9x + 14 = 0$, (c) $x^2 + 3x + 2 = 0$

(d) $x - \dfrac{2}{x} = 1$, (e) $x - \dfrac{3}{x} = 2$, (f) $\dfrac{x^2}{4 - x} = 2$

4.10   The gas phase equilibrium

$$PCl_5(g) \rightleftharpoons PCl_3(g) + Cl_2(g)$$

is set up by heating PCl_5 in a closed vessel. The equilibrium constant, K, is equal to 2 at the prevailing temperature where K is defined by

$$K = \frac{[PCl_3][Cl_2]}{[PCl_5]} = 2$$

If the initial concentration of PCl_5 is $2\,\text{mol}\,L^{-1}$ and, at equilibrium, the concentrations of PCl_3 and Cl_2 are each denoted by x, then the concentration of PCl_5 present at equilibrium will be $2 - x$. By inserting these expressions in the equation given above for the equilibrium constant K, solve the resulting quadratic equation in x and hence determine the concentration of PCl_5 at equilibrium.

4.11   The dissociation of a weak acid, HA, in solution can be represented by

$$HA \rightleftharpoons H^+ + A^-$$

and the acid dissociation constant, K_a, is defined by

$$K_a = \frac{[H^+][A^-]}{[HA]}$$

In such a solution, $[H^+] = [A^-]$, and [HA], the concentration of undissociated acid at equilibrium, is equal to the total concentration of acid less that which has dissociated, i.e. $[HA] = c - [H^+]$, where c is the total concentration of acid.

(a) Write down an expression for K_a in terms of c and $[H^+]$ only.
(b) Solve the equation derived in (a) to find the value of $[H^+]$ in a solution of formic acid for which $c = 10^{-3}\,\text{mol}\,L^{-1}$ and the acid dissociation constant, K_a, is equal to 1.77×10^{-4} at $25°C$.

4.12   Determine the values of x and y that satisfy the following pairs of equations:

(a) $2x + y = 1$ and $4x - y = 5$
(b) $2x - y = 1$ and $x + 2y = 8$
(c) $2x + 3y = 2$ and $6x - 6y = 1$
(d) $2x - 2y = 1$ and $4x - y = -1$

4.13 Determine the values of x and y that satisfy the following pairs of equations

(a) $2e^x + y = 3.44$ and $e^x - y = 0.22$
(b) $2 \ln x + 2y = 4.218$ and $\ln x + 3y = 3.109$
(c) $\ln 2x + 2y = 2.192$ and $\ln x + y = 1.298$

4.14 A solution containing two light-absorbing solutes is studied by absorption spectrometry at two wavelengths with the intention of determining the concentration of each solute. When cells with a pathlength of 1 cm are used, the measured absorbance is related to the concentrations c_a and c_b of the solutes a and b by

$$A_1 = \varepsilon_{a1} c_a + \varepsilon_{b1} c_b \qquad \text{at the first wavelength}$$

and

$$A_2 = \varepsilon_{a2} c_a + \varepsilon_{b2} c_b \qquad \text{at the second wavelength.}$$

If $A_1 = 1.7$ and $A_2 = 1.2$, and the molar absorptivities at the two wavelengths are $\varepsilon_{a1} = 8000$ and $\varepsilon_{b1} = 1800$ at the first wavelength and $\varepsilon_{a2} = 6000$ and $\varepsilon_{b2} = 1200$ at the second wavelength, all in units of $\text{mol}^{-1}\,\text{L}\,\text{cm}^{-1}$ (see Chapter 1, Section 1.6), determine the values of the concentrations c_a and c_b.

4.15 When two liquids with densities of ρ_1 and ρ_2 are mixed, the total mass of the mixture is given by

$$\text{total mass, } m = \rho_1 V_1 + \rho_2 V_2$$

where V_1 and V_2 are the volumes of the liquids that are mixed together. If m is equal to 25.4 g when $V_1 = 10\,\text{mL}$ and $V_2 = 20\,\text{mL}$, and is equal to 17.2 g when $V_1 = 10\,\text{mL}$ and $V_2 = 10\,\text{mL}$, calculate the values of ρ_1 and ρ_2.

4.16 Write out each of the following expressions as a sum of partial fractions

(a) $\dfrac{1}{(1 - 2x)(1 + x)}$, (b) $\dfrac{1}{(1 - x)(1 + x)}$, (c) $\dfrac{1}{(1 - 2x)(2 - x)}$

4.17 Evaluate the following products of imaginary numbers

(a) $i \times 2i$, (b) $3i \times (-i)$, (c) $(-2i) \times (-3i)$, (d) $i^2 \times (-2i)$

4.18 Find the imaginary or complex values of x that satisfy the following equations

(a) $x^2 + 2 = 0$, (b) $x^2 - 2x + 5 = 0$, (c) $x^2 + 4x + 5 = 0$

4.19 Evaluate the following products of complex numbers

(a) $(1 + 3i)(1 + i)$, (b) $(2 + i)(1 - 3i)$, (c) $(i - 1)(4 - i)$, (d) $i(2 + i)$

4.20 Write out the complex conjugates of the following expressions

(a) $(2 - 2i)$, (b) $1 + e^{ix}$, (c) $\exp(3 - 2ix)$, (d) $3i$

5 Differential calculus

Gradients of curves and first derivatives

The way in which a variable y depends upon some other variable x can often be specified by a functional relationship between y and x. Examples of such relationships are $y = 2x^2$, $y = 3.4x + 2.8$, $y = 4e^{-0.1x}$, and so on. Given a particular value of x, we can calculate the corresponding value of y from the functional relationship between the two. In such cases, we would say that y is a function of x, and this fact is often expressed by $y = f(x)$ where $f(x)$ (referred to as 'f of x') represents whatever the appropriate function is. For example, if $y = 2x^2$, then $f(x) = 2x^2$ in this case. However, in many problems, we are less interested in the value of y corresponding to a particular value of x than in the extent to which y changes as x is varied. For example, in studies of chemical kinetics, one is generally more interested in how rapidly a concentration changes with time than in the value of the concentration at a particular time.

Information about how a variable y varies as x is varied is contained in a graph of y plotted against x as shown in Figure 5.1. It is evident from this figure that, corresponding to the same variation in x, y varies more at point Q, at which the curve is inclined steeply upwards, than at point P. If we wanted a quantitative measure of the extent to which y varies as x varies at the position where $x = x_1$ we could construct a tangent to the curve at that point and measure its gradient. The gradient of the tangent is equal to a/b and its value tells us by how much y changes for a unit change in the value of x when $x = x_1$. Differential calculus is one way of finding the value of such a gradient accurately without having to draw a graph. Calculus has many other applications but, in the early stages of its study, its graphical interpretation is possibly most instructive.

The procedure by which a value for the gradient is found is illustrated with the aid of Figure 5.2. We imagine a chord to be drawn from the point A that is situated on the curve at $x = x_1$ to another point B. The gradient

Figure 5.1

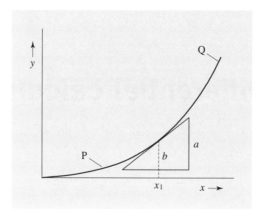

of this chord is equal to $\Delta y / \Delta x$ where Δy (delta y) is the change in the value of y that results from a change of Δx in the value of x:

$$\text{gradient of chord AB} = \frac{\Delta y}{\Delta x}$$

This gradient is not the same as the gradient of the tangent shown in Figure 5.1 but, if we allow the point B to move closer to A to some position such as B$'$, the gradient will become closer to that of the tangent:

$$\text{gradient of chord AB}' = \frac{\Delta y'}{\Delta x'}$$

If we now consider the effect of B moving closer and closer to A, it becomes apparent that the gradient of the chord will approach closer and closer to the gradient of the tangent, which is the quantity that we

Figure 5.2

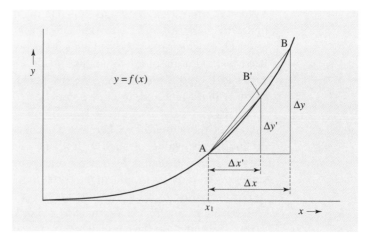

wish to determine. In symbols, the process described is denoted by

$$\underset{\Delta x \to 0}{\text{Lim}} \frac{\Delta y}{\Delta x}$$

which represents the **limiting value** of the ratio $\Delta y / \Delta x$ as Δx approaches zero, or as B approaches A. This quantity is equal to the gradient of the tangent shown in Figure 5.1 and it is the quantity that we seek. Usually this limit is written in more compact form as follows

$$\frac{dy}{dx} = \underset{\Delta x \to 0}{\text{Lim}} \frac{\Delta y}{\Delta x}$$

in which the left side is referred to as 'dy by dx' and its meaning is defined by this equation. It should not be thought of as some quantity dy divided by another quantity dx, although there are situations in which it is regarded as being approximately equal to the ratio $\Delta y / \Delta x$ when Δx is very small but still finite. In order to determine a value for this quantity, we must find an expression for Δy. This is done by noting that at the point A in Figure 5.2 the value of y is equal to $f(x_1)$, and at the point B the value of y is denoted by $y + \Delta y$ and is equal to $f(x_1 + \Delta x)$. The difference between these two values is

$$\Delta y = f(x_1 + \Delta x) - f(x_1)$$

so that we can write

$$\left(\frac{dy}{dx}\right)_{\text{at } x = x_1} = \underset{\Delta x \to 0}{\text{Lim}} \frac{f(x_1 + \Delta x) - f(x_1)}{\Delta x}$$

The quantity so defined is the **first derivative** of y with respect to x and this definition can be used to evaluate the first derivative for particular types of function, $f(x)$. For example, if $f(x) = x^2$, then $f(x_1 + \Delta x) = (x_1 + \Delta x)^2$ so that

$$\frac{f(x_1 + \Delta x) - f(x_1)}{\Delta x} = \frac{(x_1 + \Delta x)^2 - x_1^2}{\Delta x}$$

Expanding the bracket on the top line of the right side of this equation gives

$$\frac{f(x_1 + \Delta x) - f(x_1)}{\Delta x} = \frac{x_1^2 + 2x_1 \Delta x + (\Delta x)^2 - x_1^2}{\Delta x}$$

$$= 2x_1 + \Delta x$$

If we now consider the value of this quantity as Δx approaches zero we see that

$$\left(\frac{d}{dx} f(x)\right)_{\text{at } x = x_1} = \underset{\Delta x \to 0}{\text{Lim}} \frac{f(x_1 + \Delta x) - f(x_1)}{\Delta x}$$

$$= 2x_1 \qquad \text{when } f(x) = x^2$$

This would usually be written more compactly and for any value of x as

$$\frac{dx^2}{dx} = 2x$$

At the point $x = 3.2$, the graph $y = x^2$ would have a gradient of $2 \times 3.2 = 6.4$. In a similar way, we could find the gradient for any other value of x without having to draw the graph. For any value of x in general, the first derivative of a function $f(x)$ can be found from the definition

$$\frac{d}{dx} f(x) = \underset{\Delta x \to 0}{\text{Lim}} \frac{f(x + \Delta x) - f(x)}{\Delta x} \tag{5.1}$$

The first derivative of a function $f(x)$ is sometimes written as $f'(x)$, that is

$$\frac{d}{dx} f(x) = f'(x)$$

We can apply definition (5.1) to the simple case, $f(x) = x$. A graph of $y = x$ would simply be a straight line inclined at $45°$ to the x-axis and so we can predict in advance that its gradient is equal to 1 for all values of x. Putting $f(x) = x$ and $f(x + \Delta x) = x + \Delta x$ into equation (5.1) gives

$$\frac{d}{dx} f(x) = \underset{\Delta x \to 0}{\text{Lim}} \frac{(x + \Delta x) - x}{\Delta x}$$

$$= \underset{\Delta x \to 0}{\text{Lim}} \frac{\Delta x}{\Delta x}$$

$$= 1, \quad \text{irrespective of the value of } x$$

If $f(x) = a$, a quantity that does not depend on x, the graph of $f(x)$ against x would be a horizontal line and its gradient would be zero. For such a quantity,

$$\frac{da}{dx} = 0$$

The cases discussed are summarized in a simple rule that enables us to determine the first derivative of any power x^n of x:

$$\frac{dx^n}{dx} = nx^{n-1} \tag{5.2}$$

The following examples illustrate typical applications of this formula:

(a) $\dfrac{\mathrm{d}x^3}{\mathrm{d}x} = 3x^2,$

(b) $\dfrac{\mathrm{d}x^{-1}}{\mathrm{d}x} = -x^{-2},$

(c) $\dfrac{\mathrm{d}}{\mathrm{d}x}\sqrt{x} = \dfrac{\mathrm{d}}{\mathrm{d}x}x^{\frac{1}{2}} = \dfrac{x^{-\frac{1}{2}}}{2} = \dfrac{1}{2\sqrt{x}}$

If a function is multiplied by a constant as in the case $y = 2x^3$, then the effect of the factor 2 can be seen by referring back to the definition in equation (5.1). The constant 2 would simply multiply the whole of the right side of this equation so that

$$\frac{\mathrm{d}}{\mathrm{d}x}(2x^3) = 2\frac{\mathrm{d}x^3}{\mathrm{d}x} = 6x^2$$

In general,

$$\frac{\mathrm{d}}{\mathrm{d}x}af(x) = a\frac{\mathrm{d}}{\mathrm{d}x}f(x) \qquad (5.3)$$

in which a does not depend upon x.

If the function to be differentiated is a sum of other functions as in the case $f(x) = x^2 + x^3$, then each of the two functions is differentiated independently:

$$\frac{\mathrm{d}}{\mathrm{d}x}f(x) = 2x + 3x^2$$

**Self test questions
5.1**

Determine the first derivatives of the following functions

(a) x^5, (b) x^7, (c) x^{-2}, (d) x^{-3}, (e) $5x^2$, (f) $6x$, (g) $3x^2 + 2$, (h) $2x + 5x^2$, (i) $x - x^{-1}$, (j) $2\sqrt{x}$

5.2   **Changes of variable (the chain rule)**

To find the first derivative of a function such as $f(x) = (2 + x^2)^3$, we could multiply out the brackets and differentiate the resulting expression term by term. This would require that we differentiate the expression on the right side of

$$(2 + x^2)^3 = x^6 + 6x^4 + 12x^2 + 8$$

While being straightforward in this case, it is clear that such a procedure could become complex and it is a simple matter to think of functions that could not be expanded so readily into a series of powers of x. An alternative approach is to consider the function to depend upon another variable such as $u = 2 + x^2$ so that $f(x)$ becomes a function of u, $f(u)$, where $f(u) = u^3$ and $u = 2 + x^2$. The limit

$$\lim_{\Delta x \to 0} \frac{\Delta f}{\Delta x}$$

can now be written as

$$\lim_{\Delta x \to 0} \frac{\Delta f}{\Delta u} \frac{\Delta u}{\Delta x}$$

and since Δu approaches zero as Δx approaches zero, this can be written as

$$\frac{\mathrm{d}}{\mathrm{d}x} f(x) = \frac{\mathrm{d}f(u)}{\mathrm{d}u} \frac{\mathrm{d}u}{\mathrm{d}x} \qquad (5.4)$$

This is sometimes referred to as the **chain rule** for differentiation. In the case being considered

$$u = 2 + x^2$$

so that

$$\frac{\mathrm{d}u}{\mathrm{d}x} = 2x,$$

and

$$f(u) = u^3$$

so that

$$\frac{\mathrm{d}}{\mathrm{d}x} f(u) = 3u^2$$

and from equation (5.4)

$$\frac{\mathrm{d}}{\mathrm{d}x} f(x) = 3u^2 \times 2x = 6x(2+x^2)^2$$

A case in which it is necessary to change the variable is the differentiation of the function $f(x) = \sqrt{1 + x^2}$ or $(1 + x^2)^{1/2}$. Here, a suitable change of variable would be $u = 1 + x^2$, so that the function becomes $f(u) = \sqrt{u}$

or $u^{1/2}$. Then

$$\frac{du}{dx} = 2x \quad \text{and} \quad \frac{d}{du} f(u) = \frac{u^{-\frac{1}{2}}}{2} = \frac{1}{2\sqrt{u}}$$

giving

$$\frac{d}{dx} f(x) = \frac{d}{du} f(u) \frac{du}{dx} = \frac{x}{\sqrt{1 + x^2}}$$

Self test questions 5.2

Determine the first derivatives of the following functions

(a) $(2 + 3x)^4$, (b) $1/(1 + 2x)$, (c) $x^2 - 1/(1 - x)$, (d) $\sqrt{1 - 2x^2}$, (e) $1/\sqrt{1 - x^2}$

5.3   The derivative of the exponential function

The effect of differentiating the exponential function e^x can be found by considering the series expansion of this function referred to in Chapter 2:

$$e^x = 1 + x + \frac{x^2}{2!} + \frac{x^3}{3!} + \frac{x^4}{4!} + \cdots \text{etc.}$$

Differentiating each term on the right side of this equation gives

$$\frac{de^x}{dx} = 0 + 1 + x + \frac{x^2}{2!} + \frac{x^3}{3!} + \cdots \text{etc.}$$

It can be seen that the effect of differentiating the series expansion is to reproduce the original series. Although each term in the differentiated series is shifted one position to the right, since the number of terms is infinite, the two series are identical. The exponential function has the remarkable property that

$$\frac{de^x}{dx} = e^x \tag{5.5}$$

In practice, the exponential function rarely occurs in the form e^x but is more likely to appear as $A e^{ax}$ in which A and a are constants. The effect on the derivative of the constant A is simply to multiply it by A as indicated in equation (5.3):

$$\frac{d}{dx} A e^{ax} = A \frac{de^{ax}}{dx}$$

The effect of the constant a that appears inside the exponential function can be determined by regarding the exponential as a function of the variable u where $u = ax$. From equation (5.4) we then have

$$\frac{d}{dx}e^{ax} = \frac{de^u}{du}\frac{du}{dx} = a\,e^{ax}$$

Differentiating e^{ax} with respect to x gives the same result as multiplying e^{ax} by a. These results can be summarised in

$$\frac{d}{dx}A e^{ax} = aA\,e^{ax} \tag{5.6}$$

**Self test questions
5.3**

Find the first derivatives of the following functions

(a) e^{-x}, (b) $2e^{3x}$, (c) $e^x + e^{-x}$, (d) $e^{(1+x)}$, (e) $\exp(x^2)$

Note: In (e), it is necessary to change the variable to $u = x^2$. A change of variable may also be employed in (d) but is not necessary.

An important feature of equation (5.6) is that it indicates that any equation of the general form

$$\frac{dy}{dx} = ay \tag{5.7}$$

has a solution of the form $y = A e^{ax}$. Equation (5.7) is an example of a **differential equation** and it is an equation that appears frequently in the physical sciences. Note that the constant A does not appear in equation (5.7) and it is not determined from it. Any value of A could be used and $y = A e^{ax}$ would still be a solution of the differential equation. The value of A is determined by the characteristics of the process that is described by the solution $y = A e^{ax}$, in particular, the value of y when $x = 0$. An example of the occurrence of this equation is in the description of first order chemical reactions of the type

$$A \longrightarrow \text{product}$$

The rate at which the concentration of the reactant A changes is given by

$$\frac{d[A]}{dt} = -k[A] \tag{5.8}$$

This equation indicates that the rate at which [A] is changing at a particular time is proportional to the value of [A] at that time. The proportionality constant is $-k$ and k is known as the rate constant for the reaction, and the negative sign indicates that [A] *decreases* as time, t, increases. By identifying [A] with y, t with x and $-k$ with a in equation (5.7), we can immediately write down the solution to equation (5.8) as

$$[A] = [A]_0 \, e^{-kt}$$

which was discussed in Section 2.4 of Chapter 2. When $t = 0$, $e^{-kt} = 1$ and $[A] = [A]_0$. This shows that the constant $[A]_0$ is the initial concentration of the reactant A.

Self test questions
5.4

Write down the solution to the reaction rate equation

$$\frac{d[A]}{dt} = -k[A]$$

for a reaction in which the initial concentration of A is $0.1 \, \text{mol L}^{-1}$ and $k = 0.01 \, \text{s}^{-1}$

5.4   **The derivative of the logarithmic function**

The function $y = \ln x$ can be inverted to give $x = e^y$. The derivative of this inverted function with respect y is given by

$$\frac{dx}{dy} = e^y$$

We can now utilise the fact that $dy/dx = 1/(dx/dy)$ to give

$$\frac{dy}{dx} = \frac{1}{e^y} = \frac{1}{x}$$

or

$$\frac{d}{dx} \ln x = \frac{1}{x} \tag{5.9}$$

It should be noted here that since $\ln(ax) = \ln a + \ln x$, if a is a constant, then

$$\frac{d}{dx} \ln(ax) = \frac{d \ln x}{dx} = \frac{1}{x}$$

5.5	The derivatives of the sin and cos functions

As with the exponential function, the derivatives of the sine and cosine functions can be obtained by considering the series expansions of these functions which were discussed in Chapter 2:

$$\sin x = x - \frac{x^3}{3!} + \frac{x^5}{5!} - \frac{x^7}{7!} + \cdots \tag{5.10}$$

$$\cos x = 1 - \frac{x^2}{2!} + \frac{x^4}{4!} - \frac{x^6}{6!} + \cdots \tag{5.11}$$

These series expansions are valid when x is expressed in radians. Differentiating equation (5.10) with respect to x gives

$$\frac{d}{dx}\sin x = 1 - \frac{x^2}{2!} + \frac{x^4}{4!} - \frac{x^6}{6!} + \cdots$$

the right side of which is the series expansion for $\cos x$. We conclude that

$$\boxed{\frac{d}{dx}\sin x = \cos x} \tag{5.12}$$

Similarly, differentiating equation (5.11) with respect to x gives

$$\frac{d}{dx}\cos x = 0 - x + \frac{x^3}{3!} - \frac{x^5}{5!} + \cdots$$

and the right side of this is seen to be the same as the series expansion of $\sin x$ except that each term is reversed in sign. From this we conclude that

$$\boxed{\frac{d}{dx}\cos x = -\sin x} \tag{5.13}$$

The effect of constants multiplying the function itself and multiplying the variable x is similar to the case of the exponential function:

$$\boxed{\begin{aligned} \frac{d}{dx}A\sin ax &= Aa\cos ax \qquad \text{and} \\ \frac{d}{dx}A\cos ax &= -Aa\sin ax \end{aligned}} \tag{5.14}$$

in which A and a are constants.

The derivative of a power of either the sine or cosine functions can be determined by changing the variable of differentiation. For example, the function $\sin^2 x$ (which is really $(\sin x)^2$) can be written as u^2 where $u = \sin x$. Differentiation of $\sin^2 x$ can then proceed using the chain rule:

$$\frac{d}{dx}\sin^2 x = \frac{du^2}{du}\frac{du}{dx}$$

$$= 2u\cos x$$

$$= 2\sin x\cos x$$

Self test questions 5.5

Write down the first derivatives of the following functions

(a) $2\sin x$, (b) $2\sin 2x$, (c) $-\cos 3x$, (d) $\sin 2x + \cos 2x$, (e) $\sin x^2$

The first derivatives of the elementary functions are summarised below:

$$\frac{dx^n}{dx} = nx^{(n-1)}$$

$$\frac{d}{dx}e^{ax} = a\,e^{ax}$$

$$\frac{d}{dx}\ln ax = \frac{1}{x}$$

$$\frac{d}{dx}\sin ax = a\cos ax, \qquad \frac{d}{dx}\cos ax = -a\sin ax$$

5.6 | **The derivatives of products**

A product such as $x\,e^x$ cannot be differentiated using the results obtained so far. In general, we can denote such a product by $f(x)g(x)$ in which $f(x)$ and $g(x)$ are both functions of x. The definition of a derivative

$$\frac{d}{dx}f(x) = \underset{\Delta x \to 0}{\mathrm{Lim}}\frac{f(x+\Delta x)-f(x)}{\Delta x}$$

can be used for the product but we must replace $f(x+\Delta x)$ by $f(x+\Delta x)g(x+\Delta x)$ and $f(x)$ by $f(x)g(x)$. Writing $f(x)g(x)$ as fg in the interests of compactness, this gives

$$\frac{d}{dx}fg = \underset{\Delta x \to 0}{\mathrm{Lim}}\frac{f(x+\Delta x)g(x+\Delta x)-f(x)g(x)}{\Delta x}$$

The expression within the limit sign can be rewritten as

$$\left(\frac{f(x+\Delta x)-f(x)}{\Delta x}\right)g(x+\Delta x)+\left(\frac{g(x+\Delta x)-g(x)}{\Delta x}\right)f(x)$$

That this is so can easily be demonstrated by multiplying out the brackets. In the limit of Δx approaching zero, this expression reduces to the right side of

$$\frac{d}{dx}f(x)g(x) = g(x)\frac{df(x)}{dx} + f(x)\frac{dg(x)}{dx} \qquad (5.15)$$

Applying this to the product $x\,e^x$ by identifying $f(x)$ with x and $g(x)$ with e^x we obtain

$$\frac{d}{dx}f(x) = \frac{dx}{dx} = 1, \qquad \frac{d}{dx}g(x) = \frac{de^x}{dx} = e^x$$

and

$$\frac{d}{dx}xe^x = e^e + xe^x = e^x(1+x)$$

A similar method can be adopted to find the derivative of a quotient of two functions, $f(x)/g(x)$. However, this case can be dealt with by regarding the quotient as a product of $f(x)$ and $1/g(x)$. For example, the quotient e^x/x can be considered to be a product of e^x and $1/x$. Identifying $f(x)$ with $1/x$ and $g(x)$ with e^x in equation (5.15) we obtain

$$\frac{d}{dx}f(x) = \frac{dx^{-1}}{dx} = -\frac{1}{x^2}, \qquad \frac{d}{dx}g(x) = \frac{de^x}{dx} = e^x$$

and

$$\frac{d(e^x/x)}{dx} = -\frac{e^x}{x^2} + \frac{e^x}{x}$$

Self test questions
5.6

Determine the derivatives of the following products

(a) $x\,e^{2x}$, (b) $x^2\cos x$, (c) $x\ln x$, (d) $x^2\sin 2x$, (e) $(\sin x)/x$

5.7   **The effect of small variations**

The volume, V, of a cube the sides of which are of length x is given by the formula

$$V = x^3$$

The question that we wish to consider relates to the effect on the volume of a *small* change in the value of x. If the value of x was to increase to $x + \Delta x$, where Δx represents a small change in the value of x, the resulting increase in volume, ΔV, would be

$$\Delta V = (x + \Delta x)^3 - x^3$$
$$= x^3 + 3x^2 \Delta x + 3x(\Delta x)^2 + (\Delta x)^3 - x^3$$
$$= 3x^2 \Delta x + 3x(\Delta x)^2 + (\Delta x)^3$$

This expression is exact but, in practice, only the first term is significant when the change Δx is small in relation to x. For example, if x was equal to 2 cm and $\Delta x = 0.1$ cm, the sizes of the terms are as follows:

$$\Delta V = 1.2 + 0.06 + 0.001$$

Terms containing higher powers of the small quantity Δx are smaller in magnitude and are often neglected, giving the result $\Delta V = 1.2$ cm approximately. This result can be arrived at using the approximate formula

$$\Delta V = \frac{\mathrm{d}V}{\mathrm{d}x} \Delta x \tag{5.16}$$

In the case being considered, $V = x^3$ so that

$$\frac{\mathrm{d}V}{\mathrm{d}x} = 3x^2 \quad \text{and} \quad \Delta V = 3x^2 \Delta x$$

The general approximate expression for any function $f(x)$ is

$$\boxed{f(x + \Delta x) = f(x) + \frac{\mathrm{d}f}{\mathrm{d}x} \Delta x} \tag{5.17}$$

This expresses the fact that the value of the function when at $x + \Delta x$ is approximately equal to its value at x plus the small difference arising from the change Δx in the value of x. The approximation becomes more exact the smaller Δx is in relation to x. It should be noted that if Δx represents a *decrease* in the value of x, its value will be negative.

Self test questions 5.7

The area, A, of a circular disk of radius r is given by the expression

$$A = \pi r^2$$

By differentiating this, find an expression for the increase in area when r increases by a small amount Δr. Find the increase in area of a disk of radius 2 cm when $\Delta r = 0.01$ cm.

5.8 Higher order derivatives

Having differentiated a function once, we can differentiate it again to find the **second derivative**. Differentiating a third time would give us the third derivative, and so on. For example, the first, second and third derivatives of the function x^4 are

$$\frac{dx^4}{dx} = 4x^3, \quad \frac{d^2}{dx^2}x^4 = \frac{d}{dx}(4x^3) = 12x^2, \quad \frac{d^3}{dx^3}x^4 = \frac{d}{dx}(12x^2) = 24x$$

Note the notation d^2/dx^2 and d^3/dx^3 used to denote the second and third derivatives. The indices 2 and 3 *do not mean* that some quantity d must be squared or cubed, but simply indicate that the operation of differentiation should be performed twice or three times in succession. Derivatives higher than the second do not occur frequently in the context of chemistry. The first derivative of a function $f(x)$ tells us how the function changes as the variable x changes and it can be identified with the gradient of a plot of $f(x)$ against x at a particular point. The second derivative tells us how the *gradient* changes as x changes.

The second derivatives of the exponential and trigonometric functions are given below.

$$\frac{d^2 e^{ax}}{dx^2} = a^2 e^{ax} \tag{5.18}$$

$$\frac{d^2}{dx^2}\sin ax = -a^2 \sin ax \tag{5.19}$$

$$\frac{d^2}{dx^2}\cos ax = -a^2 \cos ax \tag{5.20}$$

and they are obtained simply by differentiating the functions e^{ax}, $\sin ax$ and $\cos ax$ twice in succession. These particular relationships are unusual in that the effect of differentiating the function twice in succession is to produce the original function multiplied by a constant. Equations of this sort appear in quantum theory. Equations (5.19) and (5.20) also appear in the description of oscillatory phenomena. These two equations have the general form

$$\frac{d^2y}{dx^2} = -a^2y \qquad (5.21)$$

and equations (5.19) and (5.20) tell us that it has two solutions which can be written as $y = \sin ax$ and $y = \cos ax$ or, more generally, $y = A \sin ax$ and $y = A \cos ax$ where A is a constant. Equation (5.21) is known as a **second order differential equation** because the highest derivative that it contains is a second derivative. It is often found written with the variable t, representing time, instead of x:

$$\frac{d^2y}{dt^2} = -\omega^2 y$$

This equation has the two solutions $y = A \sin \omega t$ and $y = A \cos \omega t$ and they represent the displacement of a point undergoing oscillatory motion from its equilibrium position. They could, for example, represent the oscillatory motion of an atom in a vibrating diatomic molecule. The constant ω is the angular frequency of the motion as discussed in Chapter 2.

**Self test questions
5.8**

Determine the second derivatives of the following functions

(a) $2x^3$, (b) $x^3 + 2x^2$, (c) $4 \sin 2x$, (d) $3(\sin 2x + \cos 2x)$, (e) $3e^{-2x}$

5.9 | **Maximum and minimum values of functions**

A plot of a curve showing local maxima or minima is shown in Figure 5.3. These points are referred to as local maxima or minima because they may have this property only in their immediate vicinity. Point A is a local minimum but point C clearly corresponds to a smaller value of y. At each of the points A, B and C, the gradient of the curve is zero as indicated by the horizontal tangents. As the gradient is equal to the first derivative, dy/dx, a condition that obtains at these points is $dy/dx = 0$. This condition enables us to calculate the values of x_1, x_2 and x_3 at which the maxima or minima occur.

For example, the function $y = x^2 - 2x$ has a derivative with respect to x given by

$$\frac{dy}{dx} = 2x - 2$$

Figure 5.3

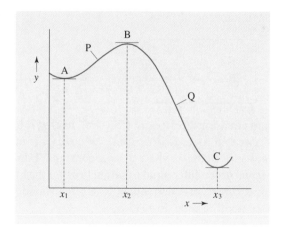

Equating this to zero gives the value $x = 1$ at which a maximum or a minimum occurs. To find out which it is, we note that in the vicinity of point A, the gradient of the curve changes from being negative to the left of A to being positive to the right. In other words, the gradient is increasing as x increases in the neighbourhood of A. As the second derivative is a measure of the way in which the gradient changes, the second derivative, d^2y/dx^2, will be a positive quantity at A. Conversely, at B the second derivative will be negative. The condition for a local maximum is therefore

$$\frac{dy}{dx} = 0 \quad \text{and} \quad \frac{d^2y}{dx^2} \quad \text{is negative} \tag{5.22}$$

and at a local minimum

$$\frac{dy}{dx} = 0 \quad \text{and} \quad \frac{d^2y}{dx^2} \quad \text{is positive} \tag{5.23}$$

Applying these conditions to the example quoted we find that

$$\frac{d^2y}{dx^2} = 2, \quad \text{a positive quantity}$$

indicating that the function $y = x^2 - 2x$ has a minimum value at $x = 1$. In this case, there are no other values of x at which either maxima or minima occur and so the minimum that we have found is a true minimum. At the points P and Q in Figure 5.3, the gradient of the curve does not change with small variations in the value of x. These are known as **inflexion points** and at them, $d^2y/dx^2 = 0$. For $y = x^2 - 2x$, there are no values of x at which $d^2y/dx^2 = 0$ and so a plot of y against x would not exhibit inflexion points. However, for the function $y = x^3 - 6x^2$, it is readily shown that

$$\frac{d^2y}{dx^2} = 6x - 12$$

which is equal to zero when $x = 2$, at which point the function has an inflexion point.

Self test questions **5.9**	Determine the values of x for which the following functions have maxima or minima and specify whether the point is a maximum or a minimum:

(a) $2x^2 - 6x$, (b) $x^2 - 12x$, (c) $x^3 - 6x^2$

5.10	**Partial derivatives**

So far, we have discussed the differentiation of functions, $f(x)$, of a single variable x. However, in practice, there are many situations in which the value of a quantity depends upon two or more variables. For example, the pressure, P, of n moles of an ideal gas is given by the equation

$$P = \frac{nRT}{V} \tag{5.24}$$

in which R is the gas constant, T the temperature of the gas in kelvin and V its volume. In this case, P is a function of the *two* variables T and V. The derivative that shows us how the pressure changes with temperature alone is obtained by considering the volume to have a fixed value and then differentiating equation (5.24) with respect to T. Such a derivative is known as a partial derivative and it is written as

$$\left(\frac{\partial P}{\partial T}\right)_V = \frac{nR}{V} \tag{5.25}$$

The symbol ∂ is used to denote that it is a partial derivative and the subscript V outside the bracket indicates that the volume is being held constant. If we wanted to specify how the pressure varies with volume at a fixed temperature we would differentiate with respect to V and regard the temperature as a constant:

$$\left(\frac{\partial P}{\partial V}\right)_T = -\frac{nRT}{V^2} \tag{5.26}$$

If we consider the number of moles n to be a variable also, these partial derivatives would be written as

$$\left(\frac{\partial P}{\partial T}\right)_{V,n} \quad \text{and} \quad \left(\frac{\partial P}{\partial V}\right)_{T,n}.$$

Self test questions
5.10

Determine $(\partial z/\partial x)_y$ and $(\partial z/\partial y)_x$ for the following functions

(a) $z = x^2 + 2y$, (b) $z = xy + y^2$, (c) $y e^x$, (d) x/y

It was shown in Section 5.7 that if the variable x changes by a small amount Δx, the change in the value of the function $f(x)$ is given by

$$\Delta f(x) = \frac{df}{dx}\Delta x$$

The change in the value of a function $f(x, y)$ as a result of changes Δx and Δy in the values of x and y is given by

$$\Delta f(x,y) = \left(\frac{\partial f}{\partial x}\right)_y \Delta x + \left(\frac{\partial f}{\partial y}\right)_x \Delta y \qquad (5.27)$$

For values of Δx and Δy of finite size this relationship is an approximation, but it is one that can be made as accurate as one wishes it to be by allowing these quantities to become smaller. This feature underlies the convention of writing equation (5.27) down in the form of **differentials** $df(x, y)$, dx and dy:

$$df(x,y) = \left(\frac{\partial f}{\partial x}\right)_y dx + \left(\frac{\partial f}{\partial y}\right)_x dy \qquad (5.28)$$

When df is given by an expression of this sort it is referred to as an **exact differential**, signifying that the expression is a necessary consequence of the fact that the value of the function f is completely determined by the values of x and y. An application of this expression is in finding derivatives when y is defined implicitly in terms of x. For example, the function $f(x, y) = x^2 y + \sin y = 0$ defines an implicit relationship between x and y and it would be difficult to write this down in an explicit form such as $y = f(x)$, making it difficult to determine df/dx directly. However, since $f(x, y) = 0$ and $df(x, y) = 0$ we deduce from equation (5.28) that

$$\frac{dy}{dx} = -\frac{(\partial f/\partial x)_y}{(\partial f/\partial y)_x} \qquad (5.29)$$

It would also be true that $df(x, y) = 0$ if $x^2y + \sin y = $ a constant. For the function $f(x, y) = x^2y + \sin y$,

$$\left(\frac{\partial f}{\partial x}\right)_y = 2xy \quad \text{and} \quad \left(\frac{\partial f}{\partial y}\right)_x = x^2 + \cos y$$

giving

$$\frac{dy}{dx} = -\frac{2xy}{x^2 + \cos y}$$

Equation (5.28) often appears in the context of thermodynamics largely because functions that arise in the study of thermodynamics are often dependent on more than one variable. As indicated in equation (5.24), the pressure of n moles of a gas is a function of the volume and temperature of the gas, allowing us to write

$$dP(V, T) = \left(\frac{\partial P}{\partial T}\right)_V dT + \left(\frac{\partial P}{\partial V}\right)_T dV$$

$$= \frac{nR}{V}dT - \frac{nRT}{V^2}dV$$

However, one of the more common uses of exact differentials arises from the fact that if we know that some function f is a function of two variables x and y so that

$$df(x, y) = \left(\frac{\partial f}{\partial x}\right)_y dx + \left(\frac{\partial f}{\partial y}\right)_x dy$$

and we also know that $df = A\,dx + B\,dy$ where A and B are properties of the system being studied, then this allows the identification

$$A = \left(\frac{\partial f}{\partial x}\right)_y \quad \text{and} \quad B = \left(\frac{\partial f}{\partial y}\right)_x$$

For example, it is shown in texts on thermodynamics that the change in enthalpy of a system of fixed size is related to the change in entropy and the change in pressure by

$$dH = T\,dS + V\,dP$$

in which H denotes enthalpy, T temperature, S entropy, V volume and P pressure. Considering H to be a function of S and P we have

$$dH(S, P) = \left(\frac{\partial H}{\partial S}\right)_P dS + \left(\frac{\partial H}{\partial P}\right)_S dP$$

allowing the identifications

$$\left(\frac{\partial H}{\partial S}\right)_P = T \quad \text{and} \quad \left(\frac{\partial H}{\partial P}\right)_S = V \quad\quad\quad (5.30)$$

It is not obvious, but it can be shown that the following relationship holds between second partial derivatives:

$$\left[\frac{\partial}{\partial x}\left(\frac{\partial f}{\partial y}\right)_x\right]_y = \left[\frac{\partial}{\partial y}\left(\frac{\partial f}{\partial x}\right)_y\right]_x$$

On the left side, the derivative $(\partial f/\partial y)_x$ has been differentiated with respect to x holding y constant and on the right side, the derivative $(\partial f/\partial x)_y$ has been differentiated with respect to y holding x constant. This is known as **Euler's reciprocity relation** and applying it to equation (5.30) gives

$$\left(\frac{\partial T}{\partial P}\right)_S = \left(\frac{\partial V}{\partial S}\right)_P$$

which is one of several similar equations known as the Maxwell relations.

Answers to self test questions

5.1 (a) $5x^4$, (b) $7x^6$, (c) $-2/x^3$, (d) $-3/x^4$, (e) $10x$, (f) 6, (g) $6x$, (h) $2 + 10x$, (i) $1 + 1/x^2$, (j) $1/\sqrt{x}$

5.2 (a) $12(2 + 3x)^3$, (b) $-2/(1 + 2x)^2$, (c) $2x - 1/(1 - x)^2$, (d) $-2x/\sqrt{1 - 2x^2}$ (e) $x(1 - x^2)^{-\frac{3}{2}}$

5.3 (a) $-e^{-x}$, (b) $6e^{3x}$, (c) $e^x - e^{-x}$, (d) $e^{(1+x)}$, (e) $2x\exp(x^2)$

5.4 $[A] = 0.1e^{-0.01t}$

5.5 (a) $2\cos x$, (b) $4\cos 2x$, (c) $3\sin 3x$, (d) $2\cos 2x - 2\sin 2x$, (e) $2x\cos x^2$

5.6 (a) $e^{2x} + 2xe^{2x}$, (b) $2x\cos x - x^2\sin x$, (c) $1 + \ln x$, (d) $2x\sin 2x + 2x^2\cos 2x$, (e) $-(\sin x)/x^2 + (\cos x)/x$

5.7 $0.126\,\text{cm}^2$

5.8 (a) $12x$, (b) $6x + 4$, (c) $-16\sin 2x$, (d) $-12(\sin 2x + \cos 2x)$, (e) $12e^{-2x}$

5.9 (a) Minimum at $x = 1.5$, (b) Minimum at $x = 6$, (c) Maximum at $x = 0$ and a minimum at $x = 4$.

5.10 (a) $\partial z/\partial x = 2x$, $\partial z/\partial y = 2$, (b) $\partial z/\partial x = y$, $\partial z/\partial y = x + 2y$, (c) $\partial z/\partial x = ye^x$, $\partial z/\partial y = e^x$, (d) $\partial z/\partial x = 1/y$, $\partial z/\partial y = -x/y^2$

Questions   **on Chapter 5**

5.1   Determine the coordinates x and y of the point on the curve $y = 2x^2 - 3x$ at which the gradient is equal to 1.

5.2   Determine the first derivatives with respect to x of the following functions:

(a) $2x^3 + 5x + 2$, (b) $\sqrt{x} + 1/\sqrt{x}$, (c) $1/x^2 + 1/x$, (d) $4e^{-2x}$,
(f) $\ln(3x)$, (g) $3\sin 4x$, (h) $2\cos 4x$

5.3   For the chemical equilibrium

$$A \rightleftharpoons B$$

which of the following are true at equilibrium (t represents time)?

(a) $d[A]/dt$ is positive, (b) $d[B]/dt$ is zero, (c) $d[B]/dt$ is negative,
(d) $d[A]/dt$ is zero, (e) $d[A]/dt = d[B]/dt$, (f) $d[A]/dt = -d[B]/dt$

5.4   In the course of the chemical reaction

$$2A \longrightarrow B$$

which one of the following is true (t represents time)?

(a) $d[A]/dt = d[B]/dt$, (b) $d[A]/dt = -d[B]/dt$,
(c) $d[A]/dt = -2d[B]/dt$, (d) $d[B]/dt = -2d[A]/dt$.

5.5   Differentiate the following functions with respect to x

(a) $(1+x)^3 - x^2$, (b) $\sqrt{1+x^2}$, (c) $1/(1+x)$, (d) $x^2/(1+x^2)$,
(e) $\exp(1-x^2)$, (f) $\sin x/x^2$

5.6   The volume of a sphere of radius r is given by the relationship

$$\text{Volume} = \tfrac{4}{3}\pi r^3$$

If a sphere of radius equal to 10 cm expands so that the radius increases by 0.1 mm, by differentiating the above relationship, obtain a value for the increase in volume.

5.7   The rate constant k for a chemical reaction is related to the temperature in kelvin by the Arrhenius equation

$$k = A\exp\left(-\frac{E_a}{RT}\right)$$

in which A is a pre-exponential factor, E_a is the activation energy, R is the gas constant ($8.314\,\text{J K}^{-1}\,\text{mol}^{-1}$) and T is the temperature. For a particular reaction, k is $20\,\text{mol}^{-1}\,\text{L s}^{-1}$ when T is 300 K. If E_a is $50\,\text{kJ mol}^{-1}$, by differentiating the above relationship with respect to T, estimate the change in the value of k when T increases by 1 degree.

5.8 The pH of a solution in which the hydrogen ion concentration is $[H^+]$ is defined by

$$pH = -\log_{10}[H^+]$$

Show that the change in pH, ΔpH, that results from a *small* change in $[H^+]$ of $\Delta[H^+]$ is proportional to the ratio $\Delta[H^+]/[H^+]$.

5.9 Indicate which two of the following are possible solutions of the differential equation

$$\frac{dy}{dt} = -0.1y$$

(a) $y = \exp(0.1t)$, (b) $y = 2\exp(-t)$, (c) $y = 10\exp(-0.1t)$,
(d) $y = \sin(-0.1t)$, (e) $y = 4\exp(-10t)$, (f) $y = 5\exp(-0.1t)$

5.10 Determine the first derivatives of the following products of functions

(a) $x^2 e^{-x}$, (b) $x^2\sqrt{1-x}$, (c) $(1-x^2)\sin 2x$, (d) $\sin x \cos x$,
(e) $\sin^2 x$ (i.e. $(\sin x)^2$)

5.11 Determine the second derivatives of the following functions of x

(a) $2x^4$, (b) $-\sin 2x$, (c) e^{3x}, (d) $\cos 2x$, (e) $e^x + e^{-x}$, (f) $x e^{-x}$

5.12 Indicate which two of the following are possible solutions of the second order differential equation

$$\frac{d^2y}{dt^2} = -4y$$

(a) $y = 4e^{-t}$, (b) $y = 3\sin 2t$, (c) $y = 2\cos 4t$, (d) $y = 4\sin t$,
(e) $y = 6\cos 2t$, (f) $y = 4\cos t$

5.13 Determine the positions of any maxima, minima and points of inflexion of the function $y = 2x^3 + 3x^2$.

5.14 A rectangle with a fixed perimeter length of L has a longer side of length x. Show that the area of the rectangle is given by

$$\text{Area} = \frac{Lx}{2} - x^2$$

and that the area is a maximum when $x = L/4$ or, in other words, when the rectangle is a square.

5.15 The probability that a molecule in a gas has a speed v can be shown to be given by a relationship of the form

$$\text{Probability of speed } v = Av^2 \exp(-\alpha v^2)$$

in which A is a constant and $\alpha = m/2kT$, where m is the mass of the molecule, k the Boltzmann constant and T the temperature of the gas in kelvin. By differentiating this function with respect to v, show that it has a maximum at $v = (2kT/m)^{1/2}$, which can be identified with the most probable speed of a molecule.

5.16 The potential energy V arising from the forces of interaction between two molecules is often written in the form

$$V = 4\varepsilon \left\{ \left(\frac{\sigma}{r}\right)^{12} - \left(\frac{\sigma}{r}\right)^{6} \right\}$$

in which ε and σ are constants and r is the distance between the molecules. By differentiating this expression with respect to r, show that the potential has a minimum when $r = 2^{1/6}\sigma$.

5.17 Write down the partial derivatives $(\partial z/\partial x)_y$ and $(\partial z/\partial y)_x$ for the following functions

(a) $z = 2xy + 3x^2$, (b) $z = e^x/y$, (c) $z = y\ln 2x$, (d) $z = \sin(xy)$,
(e) $z = x\sin y + y\sin x$, (f) $z = \sqrt{x^2 + y^2}$

5.18 The following relationship holds between the two variables x and y:

$$x^2 y + y^2 x = 2$$

Derive an expression for dy/dx and determine its two values when $x = 1$.

5.19 The change in internal energy of a closed system is related to the change in entropy and the change in volume by

$$dU = T\,dS - P\,dV$$

in which U is internal energy, T is temperature, S is entropy, P is pressure and V is volume.

(a) Write down expressions for T and P in the form of partial derivatives of U.
(b) Using the result of (a) and the Euler reciprocity relation, derive the Maxwell relation

$$\left(\frac{\partial T}{\partial V}\right)_S = -\left(\frac{\partial P}{\partial S}\right)_V$$

6 Integral calculus

6.1

Integration as the inverse of differentiation

The process of integration can be considered to be the inverse of differentiation. The integral of a function $f(x)$ is written as

$$\int f(x)\,\mathrm{d}x = g(x)$$

in which $g(x)$ is the function that results from integrating $f(x)$. Note that the function being integrated or the **integrand** is placed between the integral sign, $\int$, and the differential $\mathrm{d}x$. The reason for this will be apparent after reading Section 6.4. That integration is the inverse of differentiation is expressed by

$$\frac{\mathrm{d}}{\mathrm{d}x}g(x) = f(x)$$

For example, the first derivative of the function $y = x^n$ is given by

$$\frac{\mathrm{d}}{\mathrm{d}x}x^n = nx^{n-1}$$

and if we integrate the right side of this equation we obtain

$$\int nx^{n-1}\mathrm{d}x = x^n$$

which is true for any value of n except $n = 0$. Dividing by n and then replacing n by $n+1$ gives the result

$$\int x^n\,\mathrm{d}x = \frac{x^{n+1}}{n+1}$$

(6.1)

which is true except when $n = -1$. For example,

$$\int x^2 \, dx = \frac{x^3}{3} \quad \text{and} \quad \int x^3 \, dx = \frac{x^4}{4}$$

If the integrand is a product of a function and a constant or a function and another function that does not depend upon the variable of integration, here denoted by x, then the constant can be taken outside the integration sign. For example,

$$\int 4x^3 \, dx = 4 \int x^3 \, dx = x^4$$

Also, the effect of integrating a sum of functions of x is to give the sum of the integrals of each function. For example,

$$\int (x^3 + x^2) \, dx = \int x^3 \, dx + \int x^2 \, dx = \frac{x^4}{4} + \frac{x^3}{3}$$

Self test questions 6.1

Determine the integrals of the following functions:

(a) x^4, (b) $4x^2$, (c) $2x + x^2$, (d) $x^3 - 3x^2$, (e) $1/x^2$, (f) $(1 + x)/x^3$

As integration is the inverse of differentiation, we can immediately write down the integrals of the elementary functions discussed in Chapter 5:

$$\frac{d}{dx} e^{ax} = a e^{ax} \quad \text{so} \quad \int e^{ax} \, dx = \frac{e^{ax}}{a}$$

$$\frac{d}{dx} \ln x = \frac{1}{x} \quad \text{so} \quad \int \frac{dx}{x} = \ln x, \quad \text{for } x > 0$$

$$\frac{d}{dx} \sin ax = a \cos ax \quad \text{so} \quad \int \cos ax \, dx = \frac{\sin ax}{a}$$

$$\frac{d}{dx} \cos ax = -a \sin ax \quad \text{so} \quad \int \sin ax \, dx = -\frac{\cos ax}{a}$$

(6.2)

Self test questions 6.2

Determine the integrals of the following functions:

(a) $2e^{3x}$, (b) e^{-2x}, (c) $4/x$, (d) $\sin 2x$, (e) $\cos 3x$, (f) $(1 - x)/x$

6.2 | **Constants of integration**

If we differentiate a constant C, then the result is zero:

$$\frac{dC}{dx} = 0 \qquad \text{when } C \text{ does not depend on } x$$

It follows that if we add any constant to a function and then differentiate the resulting sum, the outcome will be the same no matter what the value of the constant is. For example, if

$$\frac{d}{dx} g(x) = f(x)$$

then adding a constant C to $g(x)$ will have no effect on the result of differentiating the function:

$$\frac{d}{dx}(g(x) + C) = \frac{d}{dx} g(x) + \frac{dC}{dx} = f(x) \qquad \text{since} \qquad \frac{dC}{dx} = 0$$

Because of this, the result of integrating the function $f(x)$ can have added to it a constant C of unspecified size giving

$$\int f(x)\, dx = g(x) + C \tag{6.3}$$

in which C is known as the **constant of integration**. For example, it is indicated in Section 6.1 that

$$\int x^2\, dx = \frac{x^3}{3}$$

but we could just as well write

$$\int x^2\, dx = \frac{x^3}{3} + 2 \qquad \text{or} \qquad \int x^2\, dx = \frac{x^3}{3} + 5 \qquad \text{or} \qquad \int x^2\, dx = \frac{x^3}{3} + C$$

where C is any constant. Differentiating the right sides of these three equations would always give the same result, x^2. In what follows, integration constants will often be omitted for reasons of compactness when indefinite integrals are executed. However, in the application of such integrations to problems they should always be taken into account. In the solution of actual problems, the value of the constant of integration would be determined by constraints that apply to the problem being considered. Such constraints are usually referred to as **boundary conditions.** An example of how such conditions arise in practice is given in the next section.

The integration of the rate equation for first order chemical reactions

That integration is the inverse of differentiation is useful because the mathematical description of physical processes is often given in the form of differential equations which must be 'undifferentiated' or integrated in order to obtain a useful solution. For example, as has already been discussed in Chapter 5, the kinetics of a first order chemical reaction of the sort

A $\longrightarrow$ product

can be described by the differential equation

$$\frac{d[A]}{dt} = -k[A]$$

in which k is a constant known as the rate constant. This differential equation is the starting point in analysing the kinetic behaviour of reactions of this sort. Formal integration of this equation would proceed according to the following steps. The differential equation is rearranged so that the function of the variable [A] and the differential d[A] appear on one side, and functions of the variable t and the differential dt appear on the other. In this case, there are no explicit functions of t:

$$\frac{d[A]}{[A]} = -k\,dt$$

This equation is now integrated:

$$\int \frac{d[A]}{[A]} = -k \int dt$$

From the results given in equations (6.2), the integral on the left side is equal to ln[A]. The integral on the right side is simply equal to t as indicated below:

$$-k \int dt = -kt$$

To one side, we must add an unspecified constant of integration C (it is not necessary to add a constant to both sides) so that:

$$\ln[A] = -kt + C$$

The value of the constant C is determined by noting that when the reaction begins at the time $t = 0$, the concentration of A is equal to its initial value which will be denoted by $[A]_0$. Putting t equal to zero then gives

$$\ln[A]_0 = C$$

so that

$$\ln[A] = -kt + \ln[A]_0$$

or

$$\ln[A] - \ln[A]_0 = -kt$$

This can be written as

$$\ln\left(\frac{[A]}{[A]_0}\right) = -kt \qquad \text{or} \qquad \frac{[A]}{[A]_0} = e^{-kt}$$

or

$$[A] = [A]_0\, e^{-kt}$$

This is the same result that was obtained in Chapter 5, but there it was obtained by noting the similarity between the effect of differentiating the exponential function and the rate equation that describes a first order reaction. The method adopted here is more general and can be applied to a much wider variety of problems.

6.4	**The integral of a function as the area under a plot of the function**

The integral of a function can be given a graphical interpretation that is illustrated in Figure 6.1, which shows the curve obtained by plotting the function $y = f(x)$ against x. The area beneath the curve between the values of x from x_1 to x_2 could be found approximately by adding together the areas of the rectangular strips of width Δx. This approximate area would, of course, be less than the true area beneath the curve, but it

Figure 6.1

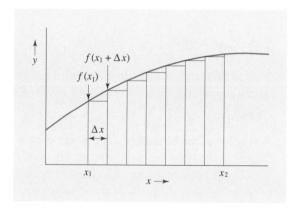

would become closer to the true area if the strips were to be reduced in width and increased in number. The value of this approximate area is equal to the sum of the areas of the strips and is given by:

$$\text{Area} = f(x_1)\Delta x + f(x_1 + \Delta x)\Delta x + f(x_1 + 2\Delta x)\Delta x$$
$$+ f(x_1 + 3\Delta x)\Delta x + \cdots \text{ etc.}$$

For the case illustrated in Figure 6.1, this sum would contain seven terms corresponding to the seven strips shown. If we were to divide up the area into a larger number of narrower strips, the result obtained would be closer to the true value. The limiting value of the area calculated as the width Δx is allowed to approach zero can be written as

$$\int_{x_1}^{x_2} f(x)\,dx = \lim_{\Delta x \to 0} (f(x_1)\Delta x + f(x_1 + \Delta x)\Delta x + f(x_1 + 2\Delta x)\Delta x$$
$$+ f(x_1 + 3\Delta x)\Delta x + \cdots)$$

in which the number of terms is equal to $(x_2 - x_1)/\Delta x$ and becomes larger as Δx becomes smaller. The **definite integral** shown on the left of this equation is equal to the area under the curve obtained by plotting the function $f(x)$ against x between the values $x = x_1$ and $x = x_2$. The origin of the symbols used to denote an integral is clearer from this interpretation of an integral than it is by considering integration to be simply the inverse of differentiation. In particular, the integration symbol, $\int$, can be seen to resemble the letter 'S' denoting summation. It is described as a definite integral because it has a well-defined value, unlike the **indefinite integrals** described earlier, the values of which were dependent upon the size of a constant of integration. The way in which the value of a definite integral is obtained can be illustrated by considering the example $f(x) = x^2$ and evaluating the area under a curve of x^2 plotted against x between the values $x = 1$ and $x = 3$. This area is given by

$$\text{Area} = \int_1^3 x^2\,dx$$
$$= \left[\frac{x^3}{3}\right]_1^3$$
$$= \frac{(3)^3}{3} - \frac{(1)^3}{3}$$
$$= \frac{27}{3} - \frac{1}{3}$$
$$= \frac{26}{3}$$
$$= 8.667$$

The **upper limit of integration**, 3, is inserted into the function $x^3/3$ to obtain 27/3, and then the **lower limit of integration**, 1, is inserted and the result of this is subtracted from 27/3 as shown. The value of a definite integral is determined by the values of the upper and lower limits of integration.

Areas beneath the x-axis

The part of the curve shown in Figure 6.1 lies entirely above the x-axis. The lengths of the strips shown are all measured along the positive portion of the y-axis (that is upwards) and the areas of these strips are therefore regarded as positive in sign. Accordingly, we consider the area between a curve and the x-axis to be positive when the curve is above the x-axis. If part of the curve lies below the x-axis as shown in Figure 6.2, then the area between that part of the curve and the x-axis is considered to be negative in sign. The area between the curve and the x-axis is negative between x_1 and x_2 and positive between x_2 and x_3. In cases where the positive and negative components are equal in magnitude, the calculated area would be zero. Such a case is illustrated in Figure 6.3 which shows a plot of the function $y = \sin x$. Integration of this function from $x = -\pi$ to $x = \pi$ would give a zero result because the negative component of the area to the left of the y-axis would exactly cancel the positive component to the right. The function $\sin x$ is an odd function of x, i.e. $\sin(-x) = -\sin x$ as illustrated in Figure 6.3. It is readily seen that if we integrate *any* odd function over a region that is symmetric about the y-axis, say from $-a$ to $+a$, then the result will be zero, that is,

$$\int_{-a}^{a} f(x)\,\mathrm{d}x = 0 \qquad \text{when } f(-x) = -f(x) \tag{6.4}$$

Figure 6.2

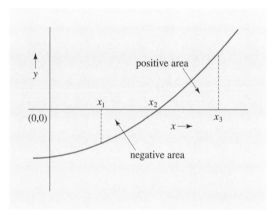

Figure 6.3

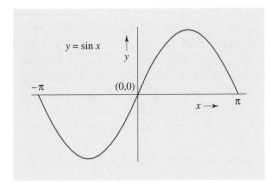

This characteristic of odd functions arises in several applications including the deduction of selection rules in spectroscopy. Notice that if $f(x)$ is an *even* function, that is $f(-x) = f(x)$, then

$$\int_{-a}^{a} f(x)\,dx = 2 \int_{0}^{a} f(x)\,dx$$

Integration can be considered to be the inverse of differentiation, or it can be considered to be a process that enables one to calculate the area under the curve obtained by plotting the function that is being integrated against its independent variable. It will not be done here, but it can be shown that these two aspects of integration are consistent with each other.

**Self test questions
6.3**

Evaluate the following definite integrals:

(a) $2\int_{1}^{2} x\,dx$, (b) $\int_{0}^{1} e^{x}\,dx$, (c) $\int_{0}^{\pi} \sin x\,dx$, (d) $\int_{0}^{a} (a - 2x)\,dx$,

(e) $\int_{0}^{\pi/2} \cos x\,dx$, (f) $\int_{1}^{3} \frac{dx}{2x}$

6.5   **The work done on an ideal gas**

Integration is required to solve differential equations, that is equations containing derivatives such as dy/dx, as was described in Section 6.3. Integration is also used in the derivation of formulae from expressions that involve small (differential) changes. For example, the work dW done *on* a gas at pressure P when its volume changes reversibly by an infinitesimal amount dV is given by

$$dW = -P\,dV \tag{6.5}$$

If the volume reduces, dV will be negative, making dW a positive quantity, consistent with the fact that work must be done on a gas to compress it. This expression is written in terms of differentials dW and dV because the pressure of a fixed quantity of a gas will in general change as its volume changes, and any method that is intended to arrive at the total work done when the volume changes by a finite amount would have to take this change in pressure into account. This would be done by integrating both sides of the equation as shown below:

$$\int dW = -\int_{V_i}^{V_f} P \, dV \tag{6.6}$$

in which the upper and lower limits of integration are the final volume V_f and the initial volume V_i respectively. The integral on the left side is simply equal to W, the total amount of work done:

$$\int dW = W$$

To proceed further with the integral on the right side of equation (6.6) we must specify how the pressure P depends upon the volume V. Assuming that the gas behaves as an ideal gas, then for n moles of gas at temperature T

$$P = \frac{nRT}{V}$$

where R is the gas constant. If we consider the case in which the temperature of the gas does not change as its volume changes (an isothermal change), then putting the expression for P into the right side of equation (6.6) gives

$$W = -nRT \int_{V_i}^{V_f} \frac{dV}{V}$$

Note that the product nRT can be taken outside the integration sign because it does not depend on the volume V. From equations (6.2), this expression for W becomes

$$W = -nRT[\ln V]_{V_i}^{V_f}$$

$$= -nRT(\ln V_f - \ln V_i)$$

$$= nRT \ln\left(\frac{V_i}{V_f}\right)$$

which is the desired result. Knowing the initial and final volumes of the gas, we could use this result to calculate the work done on the gas during an isothermal change in volume.

6.6   **Integration by change of variable**

Many integrals can be executed by changing the variable of integration to some other convenient variable. For example, the integral

$$\int x\sqrt{1+x^2}\,\mathrm{d}x$$

can be integrated by identifying $(1+x^2)$ with a variable u. We then have

$$u = (1+x^2), \qquad \frac{\mathrm{d}u}{\mathrm{d}x} = 2x \qquad \text{or, in differential form, } \mathrm{d}u = 2x\,\mathrm{d}x$$

Writing the integral in terms of the variable u gives

$$\frac{1}{2}\int \sqrt{u}\,\mathrm{d}u = \frac{u^{3/2}}{3} = \frac{(1+x^2)^{3/2}}{3}$$

In this case, changing the variable is advantageous because we can recognise that the factor x in the integrand is proportional to the derivative of $(1+x^2)$.

Integrals of the form

$$\int (1+ax)^n\,\mathrm{d}x$$

in which a is a constant can also be executed by changing the variable of integration. Here we would identify the variable u with $(1+ax)$ so that $\mathrm{d}u = a\,\mathrm{d}x$. The integral would then become:

$$\frac{1}{a}\int u^n\,\mathrm{d}u = \frac{u^{n+1}}{a(n+1)} = \frac{(1+ax)^{n+1}}{a(n+1)}$$

which is valid except when $n = -1$. However, the case $n = -1$ does appear in some treatments of chemical kinetics and needs to be considered. The integral in which we are interested usually appears in the form

$$\int \frac{\mathrm{d}x}{(a-x)}$$

in which a is a constant. Here we identify the variable u with $(a-x)$, so that $\mathrm{d}u = -\mathrm{d}x$. The integral is thus transformed into

$$-\int \frac{\mathrm{d}u}{u} = -\ln u$$

$$= \ln\left(\frac{1}{u}\right)$$

$$= \ln\left(\frac{1}{a-x}\right)$$

Integrals containing the trigonometric functions can also often be executed by making a suitable change of variable. For example, in the integral

$$\int \sin x \cos x \, dx$$

we can identify the variable u with $\sin x$ so that $du = \cos x \, dx$. The integral is then transformed to

$$\int u \, du = \frac{u^2}{2} = \frac{\sin^2 x}{2}$$

An extension of this kind of variable change to more general cases leads to the formulae:

$$\int \sin^n x \cos x \, dx = \frac{(\sin x)^{n+1}}{n+1}$$

$$\int \cos^n x \sin x \, dx = -\frac{(\cos x)^{n+1}}{n+1}$$

which are valid except when $n = -1$.

**Self test questions
6.4**

By making a suitable change of variable, perform the following integrations

(a) $\int (1+x)^4 \, dx$, (b) $\int x(1+x^2)^3 \, dx$, (c) $\int x e^{-x^2} \, dx$,

(d) $\int (1 - \sin x) \cos x \, dx$

6.7 **Integration by parts**

Integration by parts is a method of evaluating the integrals of products such as

$$\int x e^{2x} \, dx$$

As shown in the previous section, products can often be integrated by changing the variable of integration, but that approach would not be useful here. The method of integration by parts derives from the expression for the derivative of a product discussed in Chapter 5:

$$\frac{d}{dx} f(x)g(x) = g(x)\frac{df(x)}{dx} + f(x)\frac{dg(x)}{dx}$$

For compactness we will denote the functions $f(x)$ and $g(x)$ simply by f and g on the understanding that both f and g are functions of x. Integrating both sides of this equation with respect to x:

$$\int \frac{dfg}{dx}\,dx = \int g\frac{df}{dx}\,dx + \int f\frac{dg}{dx}\,dx \tag{6.7}$$

The integral on the left of this equation can be evaluated immediately as

$$\int \frac{dfg}{dx}\,dx = \int d(fg) = fg$$

allowing equation (6.7) to be rewritten as

$$\boxed{\int g\frac{df}{dx}\,dx = fg - \int f\frac{dg}{dx}\,dx} \tag{6.8}$$

This expression is useful because it is often the case that the integral on the right side is easier to evaluate than the integral on the left side. For example, returning to the integral

$$\int x\,e^{2x}\,dx$$

we could identify x with the function g and e^{2x} with the derivative df/dx that appears on the left side of equation (6.8). If $e^{2x} = df/dx$ then

$$f = \int e^{2x}\,dx = \frac{e^{2x}}{2}$$

Also, if $g = x$ then $dg/dx = 1$. Putting these results into equation (6.8) gives

$$\int x\,e^{2x}\,dx = \frac{x\,e^{2x}}{2} - \int \frac{e^{2x}}{2}\,dx$$

The integral on the right can be evaluated readily (see equations 6.2) giving

$$\int x\,e^{2x}\,dx = \frac{x\,e^{2x}}{2} - \frac{e^{2x}}{4} = \frac{e^{2x}}{2}\left(x - \frac{1}{2}\right)$$

It should be noted that the success of this method depends upon an appropriate identification of the functions g and df/dx with the functions in the product that is being integrated. In this case, we have identified g with x with the result that the derivative dg/dx on the right side of equation (6.8) is simply 1. Had we chosen to identify df/dx with x, the resulting expressions would be correct but the integrals would have been made more difficult to evaluate.

In some cases, it is necessary to carry out the process of integration by parts more than once. For example, in the evaluation of the integral

$$\int x^2 e^{2x} dx$$

we could identify g with x^2 so that dg/dx becomes $2x$. The integral on the right side of equation (6.8) would then be found to contain the product $x e^{2x}$ which could be evaluated by a further application of integration by parts as has been done above.

Integration by parts can be applied when the integrand is not written explicitly in the form of a product. For example, in the integral

$$\int \ln x \, dx$$

we can consider the integrand $\ln x$ to be a product of $\ln x$ and 1. Identifying $\ln x$ with $g(x)$ and $df(x)/dx$ with 1 gives $dg(x)/dx = 1/x$ and $f(x) = x$. Putting these into equation (6.8) we obtain:

$$\int \ln x \, dx = x \ln x - \int x \frac{1}{x} dx = x \ln x - \int dx = x \ln x - x$$

In all of the cases described above, the indefinite integrals shown could be converted to definite integrals simply by imposing suitable limits of integration. For example, in the integral of $\ln x$

$$\int_a^b \ln x \, dx = [x \ln x - x]_a^b = (b \ln b - b) - (a \ln a - a)$$

**Self test questions
6.5**

Perform the following integrations:

(a) $\int x e^{-x} dx$, (b) $\int (1-x)e^x dx$, (c) $\int x \sin x \, dx$, (d) $\int x^2 \cos x \, dx$

6.8 | **Integration using the method of partial fractions**

The method of partial fractions is used to integrate functions that appear as algebraic fractions. In the context of chemistry, integrals of this type appear in the analysis of the rate equations that describe second order chemical reactions. The kind of integral encountered is of the form

$$\int \frac{dx}{(a-x)(b-x)} \tag{6.9}$$

in which a and b are constants. The breaking up of the fraction that appears as the integrand into two separate fractions has been discussed in Section 4.9. There it was shown that by writing

$$\frac{1}{(a-x)(b-x)} = \frac{P}{(a-x)} + \frac{Q}{(b-x)}$$

we can determine that $P + Q = 0$ and $Pb + Qa = 1$. These two equations are readily solved to give

$$P = \frac{1}{(b-a)} \quad \text{and} \quad Q = -\frac{1}{(b-a)}$$

and the integral in equation (6.9) can be written as

$$\int \frac{dx}{(a-x)(b-x)} = \frac{1}{(b-a)} \left[\int \frac{dx}{(a-x)} - \int \frac{dx}{(b-x)} \right]$$

The integrals within the square brackets on the right of this equation can be executed by a simple change of variable. For the first integral we can put $u = (a-x)$ so that $du = -dx$ and

$$\int \frac{dx}{(a-x)} = -\int \frac{du}{u} = -\ln u = -\ln(a-x)$$

Similarly the second integral is

$$\int \frac{dx}{(b-x)} = -\ln(b-x)$$

We can therefore write the required integral as

$$\int \frac{dx}{(a-x)(b-x)} = \frac{1}{(b-a)} [\ln(b-x) - \ln(a-x)]$$

$$= \frac{1}{(b-a)} \ln\left(\frac{b-x}{a-x}\right) \tag{6.10}$$

The connection between this integral and second order chemical reactions of the sort

$$A + B \longrightarrow \text{product}$$

derives from the rate equation that describes such a reaction:

$$\frac{d[A]}{dt} = \frac{d[B]}{dt} = -k[A][B]$$

in which k is a rate constant. At any time during the course of the reaction, the concentrations of A and B can be written as $[A] = [A]_0 - x$ and $[B] = [B]_0 - x$ in which x is the concentration of A (or B) that has reacted at that time and $[A]_0$ and $[B]_0$ are the initial concentrations of A and B (assumed to be different). From the relationship $[A] = [A]_0 - x$ we can write

$$\frac{d[A]}{dt} = -\frac{dx}{dt}$$

and the rate equation becomes

$$\frac{dx}{dt} = k([A]_0 - x)([B]_0 - x)$$

We now write this in differential form and integrate:

$$\int_0^{x_t} \frac{dx}{([A]_0 - x)([B]_0 - x)} = k \int dt$$

in which the limits of integration for the left integral are between $x = 0$ (when the reaction starts) and $x = x_t$, the value of x at time t. This integral can be seen to have the same form as that in equation (6.9). From the result displayed in equation (6.10) we can write

$$\left[\frac{1}{[B]_0 - [A]_0} \ln \left(\frac{[B]_0 - x}{[A]_0 - x} \right) \right]_0^{x_t} = kt$$

Inserting the limits of integration then gives

$$\frac{1}{([B]_0 - [A]_0)} \ln \left(\frac{([B]_0 - x_t)[A]_0}{([A]_0 - x_t)[B]_0} \right) = kt$$

This rather complex expression shows how the concentrations of A and B change in the course of a second order reaction in which the initial concentrations of the reactants, $[A]_0$ and $[B]_0$, are not the same.

6.9   **The integration of particular functions**

Many integrations can be carried out using the methods described above, but there are some integrals that could be encountered in the study of chemistry and that have not been dealt with so far. Some of these will be dealt with in this section.

Integrals of trigonometric functions

These integrals are likely to be found in elementary treatments of quantum mechanics. Often, particular forms of the definite integrals required are tabulated in tables of integrals, but the way in which some of these results have been obtained is indicated in this section.

The integrals

$$\int \sin^2 ax \, dx \qquad \text{and} \qquad \int \cos^2 ax \, dx$$

can be executed by integration by parts or by use of the trigonometric relationships

$$\sin^2 x = \frac{1 - \cos 2x}{2} \qquad \text{and} \qquad \cos^2 x = \frac{1 + \cos 2x}{2}$$

Using the second of these approaches, the integrations are executed as shown below:

$$\int \sin^2 ax \, dx = \frac{1}{2} \int (1 - \cos 2ax) \, dx = \frac{x}{2} - \frac{\sin 2ax}{4a}$$

$$\int \cos^2 ax \, dx = \frac{1}{2} \int (1 + \cos 2x) \, dx = \frac{x}{2} + \frac{\sin 2ax}{4a}$$

The integral

$$\int x \sin^2 ax \, dx$$

can be executed by integration by parts. Referring to equation (6.8) and identifying the function g with x and df/dx with $\sin^2 ax$ we obtain $dg/dx = 1$ and the expression for f is as found above:

$$f(x) = \frac{x}{2} - \frac{\sin 2ax}{4a}$$

Putting these results into equation (6.8) gives:

$$\int x \sin^2 ax \, dx = x \left(\frac{x}{2} - \frac{\sin 2ax}{4a} \right) - \int \left(\frac{x}{2} - \frac{\sin 2ax}{4a} \right) dx$$

$$= \frac{x^2}{4} - \frac{x \sin 2ax}{4a} - \frac{\cos 2ax}{8a^2}$$

When encountered in quantum mechanics, the limits of integration imposed on this integral are usually such that only the first of the three terms given above is non-zero. For example,

$$\int_0^b x \sin^2 \left(\frac{n\pi x}{b} \right) dx = \frac{b^2}{4}$$

in which n is an integer and b is a constant.

The integral

$$\int x^2 \sin^2 ax \, dx$$

can be executed by a further application of integration by parts. In this case, we would again identify the function g with x, but df/dx would be identified with $x \sin^2 ax$. The function $f(x)$ would then be:

$$f(x) = \frac{x^2}{4} - \frac{x \sin 2ax}{4a} - \frac{\cos 2ax}{8a^2}$$

and by substituting into equation (6.8) we would have

$$\int x^2 \sin^2 ax \, dx = x\left(\frac{x^2}{4} - \frac{x \sin 2ax}{4a} - \frac{\cos 2ax}{8a^2}\right)$$
$$- \int \left(\frac{x^2}{4} - \frac{x \sin 2ax}{4a} - \frac{\cos 2ax}{8a^2}\right) dx$$

The integral appearing here can be evaluated using the methods discussed earlier to give

$$\int x^2 \sin^2 ax \, dx = \frac{x^3}{6} - \frac{x \cos 2ax}{4a^2} - \frac{x^2 \sin 2ax}{4a} + \frac{\sin 2ax}{8a^3}$$

As in the previous case, when this integral appears in quantum mechanical calculations it is usually found that the limits of integration are such that the last two terms are zero. For example

$$\int_0^b x^2 \sin^2 \left(\frac{n\pi x}{b}\right) dx = \frac{b^3}{6} - \frac{b^3}{4n^2\pi^2}$$

in which n is an integer and b is a constant.

In addition to integrals of the trigonometric functions themselves, there are other integrals of common occurrence that give rise to the inverse trigonometric functions when they are executed. The function $\alpha = \sin^{-1}(x/a)$ in which a is a constant, is the angle which has a sine value equal to x/a. The derivative

$$\frac{d}{dx} \sin^{-1}(x/a) = \frac{d\alpha}{dx}$$

can be found by noting that as $x = a \sin \alpha$, $dx/d\alpha = a \cos \alpha$, and $d\alpha/dx = 1/(a \cos \alpha)$. Using the general relationship $\sin^2 \alpha + \cos^2 \alpha = 1$, we can write

$$\frac{d}{dx} \sin^{-1}(x/a) = \frac{1}{a \cos \alpha} = \frac{1}{a\sqrt{1 - \sin^2 \alpha}} = \frac{1}{\sqrt{a^2 - a^2 \sin^2 \alpha}} = \frac{1}{\sqrt{a^2 - x^2}}$$

Accordingly

$$\int \frac{dx}{\sqrt{a^2 - x^2}} = \sin^{-1}\left(\frac{x}{a}\right)$$

It can also be shown that

$$\int \frac{\mathrm{d}x}{a^2 + x^2} = \frac{1}{a} \tan^{-1}\left(\frac{x}{a}\right)$$

Integrals of functions of the form $x^n \exp(-ax^2)$

These integrals commonly occur in statistical calculations involving the Maxwell–Boltzmann distribution function. They generally appear as definite integrals evaluated between the limits of integration $x = 0$ and $x = \infty$. The integral

$$\int e^{-ax^2} \,\mathrm{d}x$$

in which a is a constant assumed to be greater than zero, cannot be executed to give a result in terms of known functions. By making the change of variable $u = \sqrt{a}x$ it is readily shown that

$$\int e^{-ax^2} \,\mathrm{d}x = \frac{1}{\sqrt{a}} \int e^{-u^2} \,\mathrm{d}u$$

It should be noted that in making this change of variable, the limits of integration in a definite integral would also have to be changed. For example, if the upper limit of the integral in the variable x on the left was b, the upper limit in the integral in the variable u on the right would be $\sqrt{a}b$. A related definite integral has been evaluated numerically and it is known as the **error function**, erf(x):

$$\mathrm{erf}(x) = \frac{2}{\sqrt{\pi}} \int_0^x e^{-x^2} \,\mathrm{d}x$$

Values of the error function for different values of x have been tabulated. In the form in which it is most commonly encountered

$$\int_0^\infty e^{-ax^2} \,\mathrm{d}x = \frac{1}{2}\sqrt{\frac{\pi}{a}}$$

Notice that the function e^{-az^2} is an *even* function of x, that is, if x is replaced by $-x$ the value of the function is unchanged. A graph of such a function is symmetric about the vertical axis so that, regarding the integral as the area beneath such a graph

$$\int_{-\infty}^{\infty} e^{-ax^2}\,dx = 2\int_{0}^{\infty} e^{-ax^2}\,dx$$

The integral

$$\int xe^{-ax^2}\,dx$$

is readily executed by making the change of variable $u = x^2$. We then have $du = 2x\,dx$ and

$$\int xe^{-ax^2}\,dx = \frac{1}{2}\int e^{-au}\,du = -\frac{e^{-au}}{2a} = -\frac{e^{-ax^2}}{2a}$$

An attempt at executing the integral

$$\int x^2 e^{-ax^2}\,dx$$

results in the appearance of the error function referred to above. The form of the integral most often required is

$$\int_{0}^{\infty} x^2 e^{-ax^2}\,dx = \frac{1}{4a}\sqrt{\frac{\pi}{a}}$$

The integral

$$\int x^3 e^{-ax^2}\,dx$$

arises in the calculation of the average speed of molecules in a gas. It can be executed by the change of variable $u = x^2$ so that $du = 2x\,dx$. The integral then becomes

$$\frac{1}{2}\int u e^{-au}\,du$$

This can be integrated by parts to give

$$\frac{1}{2}\int u e^{-au}\,du = -\frac{e^{-au}}{2a}\left(u + \frac{1}{a}\right)$$

or

$$\int x^3 e^{-ax^2}\,dx = -\frac{e^{-ax^2}}{2a}\left(x^2 + \frac{1}{a}\right)$$

The most common form of this as a definite integral is

$$\int_{0}^{\infty} x^3 e^{-ax^2}\,dx = \frac{1}{2a^2}$$

Differential equations

First order differential equations

Examples of differential equations that are found in the study of chemistry have been given in this chapter and also in Chapter 5. The equation

$$\frac{dy}{dx} = -ay$$

is of the same form as that which describes first order chemical reactions. A trivial difference is that when this equation appears in chemical kinetics, the independent variable is denoted by t representing time whereas here we denote it by x. It is described as a first order differential equation because the highest order derivative that appears in it is the first derivative dy/dx. It has been shown in Chapter 5 and in the present chapter that this equation has the solution $y = y_0 e^{-ax}$. The differential equation that describes second order chemical reactions in which the reactants have different initial concentrations is also a first order differential equation of the form

$$\frac{dy}{dx} = k(a - x)(b - x)$$

The solution to this equation is more complex and is given in Section 6.8. A related case arises when we consider a second order chemical reaction in which the initial concentrations of the reactants are equal. An example of such a case would be dimerisation:

$$2A \longrightarrow product$$

The rate equation for this reaction can be written as

$$\frac{d[A]}{dt} = -k[A]^2$$

in which k is the rate constant (the meaning of k is defined by this equation). Integration of the equation proceeds according to

$$\int \frac{d[A]}{[A]^2} = -k \int dt$$

with the result

$$-\frac{1}{[A]} = -kt + C$$

in which C is an integration constant. Imposing the condition that the concentration $[A]$ is equal to $[A]_0$ when $t = 0$ gives $C = -1/[A]_0$ and the complete solution is then

$$\frac{1}{[A]} - \frac{1}{[A]_0} = kt$$

These first order differential equations have the general form

$$\frac{dy}{dx} = p(x)q(y)$$

in which $p(x)$ is a function of x and $q(y)$ is a function of y. In the cases described above, one of the functions $p(x)$ or $q(y)$ did not appear but, in principle, the method of integrating an equation in which they do appear is clear. For such an equation, the variables x and y are said to be separable and the equation can be solved by integration as indicated below:

$$\int \frac{dy}{q(y)} = \int p(x)\,dx$$

In principle, the approach is simple enough but, in practice, the integrations required could be difficult or even impossible to execute in some cases. An example of an equation in which the variables are separable is

$$\frac{dy}{dx} = -2xy$$

This can be integrated by rearrangement so that all functions of x appear on one side and functions of y appear on the other as in

$$\int \frac{dy}{y} = -2 \int x\,dx$$

Here, both integrals can be executed to give

$$\ln y = -x^2 + C$$

in which C is an integration constant. If the boundary conditions were such that $x = 0$ when $y = 1$ ($\ln y = 0$), then the value of the integration constant would be $C = 0$ giving the solution $y = e^{-x^2}$.

Self test questions
6.6

Solve the following differential equations all subject to the condition $y = 1$ when $x = 0$:

(a) $\dfrac{dy}{dx} = 2x$, (b) $\dfrac{dy}{dx} = 2e^{-2x}$, (c) $\dfrac{dy}{dx} = xy^2$

Second order differential equations

The differential equation

$$\frac{d^2y}{dx^2} = -a^2y$$

was discussed in Section 5.8. This equation is referred to as a second order differential equation because the highest order derivative that occurs is the second derivative d^2y/dx^2. It was shown in Section 5.8 that this equation has two independent solutions that can be written as $y = A \sin ax$ and $y = B \cos ax$ in which A and B are constants. This was shown to be the case by noting that if we differentiate either of these functions twice, the outcome is to obtain the function we started with multiplied by $-a^2$. The general solution is

$$y = A \sin ax + B \cos ax$$

The values of the constants A and B are determined by the boundary conditions that apply to the problem being considered. For example, if we know that $y = 0$ when $x = 0$ then B must have a value of 0 and the solution will be of the form $y = A \sin ax$. Solutions can also be written as $A \exp(iax)$ and $B \exp(-iax)$. Again, a general solution can be written as

$$y = A \exp(iax) + B \exp(-iax)$$

In some applications, these complex solutions are easier to manipulate. This differential equation appears in the description of oscillatory motion and also in elementary quantum theory.

Because the differential equation contains a second derivative, formal integration must be carried out in two stages. In general, the integration of second order differential equations is a more involved process than the integration of first order equations and, while being straightforward in this case, it will not be gone through here. A more general form of this equation can be written as

$$\frac{d^2y}{dx^2} + a\frac{dy}{dx} + by = 0$$

Substituting into this the trial solution $y = \exp(\beta x)$ gives the quadratic equation

$$\beta^2 + a\beta + b = 0$$

from which two values of β can be found knowing the values of a and b. Denoting these two values by β_1 and β_2 the general solution would be $y = A \exp(\beta_1 x) + B \exp(\beta_2 x)$.

Several second order differential equations are encountered in the study of physical chemistry. Usually, when these are presented in texts, they are accompanied by appropriate solutions and it is rarely necessary for the student of chemistry to delve more deeply into their derivation.

Answers to self test questions

6.1 (a) $\dfrac{x^5}{5}$, (b) $\dfrac{4x^3}{3}$, (c) $x^2 + \dfrac{x^3}{3}$, (d) $\dfrac{x^4}{4} - x^3$, (e) $-\dfrac{1}{x}$, (f) $-\dfrac{1}{x}\left(\dfrac{1}{2x} + 1\right)$

6.2 (a) $\dfrac{2e^{3x}}{3}$, (b) $-\dfrac{e^{-2x}}{2}$, (c) $4\ln x$, (d) $-\dfrac{\cos 2x}{2}$, (e) $\dfrac{\sin 3x}{3}$, (f) $\ln x - x$

6.3 (a) 3, (b) e − 1 or 1.718, (c) 2, (d) 0 , (e) 1, (f) 0.549

6.4 (a) $\dfrac{(1+x)^5}{5}$, (b) $\dfrac{(1+x^2)^4}{8}$, (c) $-\dfrac{e^{-x^2}}{2}$, (d) $\sin x - \dfrac{\sin^2 x}{2}$

6.5 (a) $-e^{-x}(1+x)$, (b) $e^x(2-x)$, (c) $\sin x - x\cos x$,
(d) $x^2\sin x + 2x\cos x - 2\sin x$

6.6 (a) $y = x^2 + 1$, (b) $y = 2 - e^{-2x}$, (c) $y = 2/(2 - x^2)$

Questions on Chapter 6

6.1 Integrate the following functions with respect to x:

(a) $3x^2 + x$, (b) $2x(1 + x^2)$, (c) $(x + 1)(x + 2)$, (d) $(2 - x)/x^3$,
(e) $x(x + 1) + 2$, (f) $3\sqrt{x}$

6.2 Integrate the following with respect to x:

(a) $(1 - e^{-x})$, (b) $(1 + e^x)/e^x$, (c) $(2 + x)/x$, (d) $(1 + \sin 2x)$,
(e) $(\cos x - 1)$, (f) $(x - 2\sin 2x)$

6.3 By making a suitable change of variable, integrate the following with respect to x:

(a) $(1 + 2x)^3$, (b) $1/(1 + x)$, (c) $(1 - x)/(1 + x)$,
(d) $\sin x(1 + \cos x)^2$, (e) $\sin x/\cos x$

6.4 Determine the areas under the following curves:

(a) $y = e^{2x}$ between $x = 0$ and $x = 1$,
(b) $y = x^2$ between $x = -1$ and $x = 1$,
(c) $y = x^3$ between $x = -1$ and $x = 1$,
(d) $y = x^3\cos x$ between $x = -\pi$ and $x = \pi$.

6.5 Integrate the following functions using integration by parts:

(a) $(1 + x)e^x$, (b) $x \ln x$, (c) $x \cos x$, (d) $e^x \sin x$

6.6 Integrate the algebraic fractions

(a) $1/[(2 - x)(3 - x)]$, (b) $1/[(1 - x)(2 - x)]$

6.7 According to the van der Waals equation of state for a non-ideal gas, the pressure of n moles of gas is related to its volume V and temperature T by the equation:

$$P = \frac{nRT}{(V - nb)} - \frac{an^2}{V^2}$$

in which R is the gas constant and a and b are constants that depend upon the gas being considered. By reference to Section 6.5, show that the work, W, done on one mole of gas that is described by this equation when it is compressed reversibly from an initial volume V_i to a final volume V_f is given by

$$W = RT \ln \left(\frac{V_i - b}{V_f - b} \right) - a \left(\frac{1}{V_f} - \frac{1}{V_i} \right)$$

6.8 The result of evaluating a definite integral of the function $f(x)$ between the limits of integration 0 and a is to give a value I as shown below

$$\int_0^a f(x) \, dx = I$$

What is the value of the integral

$$\int_{-a}^a f(x) \, dx$$

(a) if $f(x)$ is an odd function of x, that is $f(x) = -f(-x)$, (b) if $f(x)$ is an even function of x, that is $f(x) = f(-x)$.

Which of the following integrals have a value of 0?

(a) $\int_{-a}^a x e^{-x^2} \, dx$, (b) $\int_{-a}^a x^2 \cos x \, dx$,

(c) $\int_{-a}^a x \sin x \, dx$, (d) $\int_{-a}^a \sin 2x \cos x \, dx$

6.9 Show that

$$\int_{-b}^b e^{-ax^2} \, dx = \sqrt{\frac{\pi}{a}} \, \text{erf}(\sqrt{ab})$$

6.10 The Gaussian probability function can be written as $p(x) = A \exp(-x^2/2\sigma^2)$ in which A and σ are constants. This function is required to have the property

$$\int_{-\infty}^{\infty} p(x)\, dx = 1$$

When $p(x)$ is such that this is true, the function is said to be normalised. By reference to the error function (Section 6.9), show that $p(x)$ will be normalised provided that $A = 1/\sqrt{2\pi\sigma^2}$.

6.11 It is shown in elementary treatments of quantum mechanics that a particle that is constrained to move along a portion of the x-axis between $x = 0$ and $x = a$ can be described by a wavefunction that has the form

$$\Psi(x) = A \sin\left(\frac{n\pi x}{a}\right)$$

In this case, the function is said to be normalised if

$$\int_0^a \Psi^2\, dx = 1$$

Show that this will be the case if $A = \sqrt{2/a}$.

6.12 When a liquid is in equilibrium with its vapour, the vapour pressure p is related to the temperature T by the Clausius–Clapeyron equation

$$\frac{d(\ln p)}{dT} = \frac{\Delta H_e}{RT^2}$$

in which ΔH_e is the enthalpy of vaporisation and R is the gas constant. If the vapour pressure is p_0 when the temperature is T_0, show that

$$p = p_0 \exp\left\{\frac{\Delta H_e}{R}\left(\frac{1}{T_0} - \frac{1}{T}\right)\right\}$$

6.13 By integrating the first order differential equation

$$\frac{dy}{dx} = y \cos x$$

show that it has a solution $y = y_0 \exp(\sin x)$ in which y_0 is the value of y when $x = 0$.

6.14 By differentiating the function $y = A \sin ax + B \cos ax$ twice, show that it is a solution to the second order differential equation

$$\frac{d^2 y}{dx^2} = -a^2 y$$

If $y = 1$ and $dy/dx = 0$ when $x = 0$, what are the values of A and B?

6.15 By substituting an assumed solution of the form $y = \exp(\beta x)$ into each of the following second order differential equations

(a) $\dfrac{d^2y}{dx^2} + \dfrac{dy}{dx} - 2y = 0,$

(b) $\dfrac{d^2y}{dx^2} - 5\dfrac{dy}{dx} + 6y = 0$

determine the appropriate values for β for each equation and write down the forms of the general solutions.

7 Matrix algebra

Matrix algebra does not appear in many branches of chemistry, but it does arise in the application of group theory to the consequences of molecular symmetry and also in quantum theory. The treatment given here will not be one of great depth and is simply intended to enable students to become familiar with some of the basic properties of matrices so that they will have fewer problems in handling them should they study those branches of chemistry in which matrix methods are employed. It is not difficult to acquire a basic understanding of what matrices are and of how they can be manipulated but the concepts involved will be unfamiliar to some.

The notion of a matrix derives from the study of linear transformations of one set of variables to another. For example, the set of equations given below transforms the variables x, y and z into a different set denoted by p, q and r:

$$\begin{aligned} x + y + z &= p \\ 2x + y - z &= q \\ x + y + 2z &= r \end{aligned} \quad (7.1)$$

These equations would be written in matrix form as

$$\begin{bmatrix} 1 & 1 & 1 \\ 2 & 1 & -1 \\ 1 & 1 & 2 \end{bmatrix} \begin{bmatrix} x \\ y \\ z \end{bmatrix} = \begin{bmatrix} p \\ q \\ r \end{bmatrix} \quad (7.2)$$

The array of three rows each of three numbers on the left is known as a **matrix** and would often be denoted by a single letter such as **A**. The columns containing the variables x, y, and z and the variables p, q and r are referred to as **column vectors** and would also be denoted by single letters such as x and p respectively. In this compressed notation, the set of three equations given in equations (7.1) would be written as

$$\mathbf{A}x = p \quad (7.3)$$

The correspondence between equations (7.1) and their matrix representation shown in equation (7.2) can be seen if we multiply, for example, the second row of the matrix $\mathbf{A}$ into the column vector $\mathbf{x}$.

$$(2 \quad 1 \quad -1) \begin{bmatrix} x \\ y \\ z \end{bmatrix} \Rightarrow 2x + y - z = \begin{bmatrix} p \\ q \\ r \end{bmatrix} \tag{7.4}$$

The first element of the row, that is, the number 2, multiplies the variable x. The second element of the row, the number 1, multiplies the variable y and the third element of the row, -1, multiplies z. These products are then added and their sum is equal to the middle element of the column vector $\mathbf{p}$, that is, the variable q, to give the second of the equations in (7.1).

Self test questions

7.1

Write out the two equations represented by the matrix equation

$$\begin{bmatrix} 2 & 1 \\ 1 & -1 \end{bmatrix} \begin{bmatrix} x \\ y \end{bmatrix} = \begin{bmatrix} p \\ q \end{bmatrix}$$

The numbers that appear in the matrix $\mathbf{A}$, or **matrix elements**, are denoted by a_{ij} where the subscript i denotes the row in which the element occurs and the subscript j denotes the column in which it occurs. For example, in the matrix $\mathbf{A}$ shown in equation (7.2), the element $a_{23} = -1$ and the element $a_{33} = 2$. The elements in the column vector $\mathbf{x}$ would be denoted by x_j where $x_1 = x$, $x_2 = y$ and $x_3 = z$. In this notation, the procedure illustrated in equation (7.4) could be written as

$$\sum_{j=1}^{3} a_{2j} x_j = p_2$$

in which p_2 is the middle element in the column vector $\mathbf{p}$. The matrix $\mathbf{A}$ shown in equation (7.2) is described as a **square matrix** because the number of rows is equal to the number of columns. It would be said to be of order 3×3. Matrices need not always be square but, except for column vectors, most of those encountered in the context of chemistry will be.

7.1   Addition of matrices

Operations such as the addition and multiplication of matrices should be justified ultimately by reference to the linear transformations that they represent. Here, we will simply state what the rules are. Examples will be given using 2×2 matrices but the procedures referred to are readily extended to square matrices of any size.

To add together two matrices one simply adds together their corresponding elements. In order to be able to do this, the matrices being added should be of the same size, that is, they should have the same number of rows and columns. The process is readily illustrated by the following example:

$$\begin{bmatrix} 1 & 3 \\ -1 & 2 \end{bmatrix} + \begin{bmatrix} 1 & 1 \\ 2 & 2 \end{bmatrix} = \begin{bmatrix} 2 & 4 \\ 1 & 4 \end{bmatrix}$$

Writing this down in the form of matrix elements we would state that if

$$\mathbf{A} + \mathbf{B} = \mathbf{C}$$

where $\mathbf{A}$, $\mathbf{B}$ and $\mathbf{C}$ are matrices, then $a_{ij} + b_{ij} = c_{ij}$ for any values of i and j permitted by constraints imposed by the size of the matrices.

7.2 **Multiplication of a matrix by a scalar**

If we multiply a matrix by some quantity n then each element of the matrix is multiplied by n:

$$n \begin{bmatrix} a_{11} & a_{12} \\ a_{21} & a_{22} \end{bmatrix} = \begin{bmatrix} na_{11} & na_{12} \\ na_{21} & na_{22} \end{bmatrix}$$

Self test questions
7.2

Perform the addition of the following matrices:

$$3 \begin{bmatrix} 2 & 1 \\ -1 & 2 \end{bmatrix} + \begin{bmatrix} 1 & 0 \\ 0 & 1 \end{bmatrix}$$

7.3 **Matrix multiplication**

The multiplication of matrices is one of the more common operations applied to them. It is illustrated by the example involving 2×2 matrices given below:

$$\begin{bmatrix} a_{11} & a_{12} \\ a_{21} & a_{22} \end{bmatrix} \begin{bmatrix} b_{11} & b_{12} \\ b_{21} & b_{22} \end{bmatrix} = \begin{bmatrix} a_{11}b_{11} + a_{12}b_{21} & a_{11}b_{12} + a_{12}b_{22} \\ a_{21}b_{11} + a_{22}b_{21} & a_{21}b_{12} + a_{22}b_{22} \end{bmatrix} \tag{7.5}$$

The element in the *first* row and *first* column of the product, that is, the element $a_{11}b_{11} + a_{12}b_{21}$ is obtained by multiplying the elements of the first row of the first matrix, a_{11} and a_{12}, into the elements of the first column of the second matrix, b_{11} and b_{12}, in the manner required to obtain the product element shown. The element in the *first* row and *second* column of the product matrix is obtained by multiplying the elements in the first row of the first matrix, that is, a_{11} and a_{12}, into the elements of the second column of the second matrix, b_{12} and b_{22}, to give $a_{11}b_{12} + a_{12}b_{22}$. Other elements of the product matrix are obtained in a similar fashion as is indicated by inspection of equation (7.5). Representing the multiplication process by

$$\mathbf{AB} = \mathbf{C}$$

the elements of the product matrix $\mathbf{C}$ are given by

$$c_{ij} = \sum_k a_{ik}b_{kj}$$

Self test questions 7.3

Perform the following matrix multiplications

(a) $\begin{bmatrix} 2 & 1 \\ 1 & 0 \end{bmatrix} \begin{bmatrix} 1 & 1 \\ 2 & 3 \end{bmatrix}$, (b) $\begin{bmatrix} -1 & 1 \\ 0 & 2 \end{bmatrix} \begin{bmatrix} 2 & 2 \\ 1 & -1 \end{bmatrix}$

It is informative to consider how matrix multiplication is related to the transformation of variables. Suppose that we have two variables denoted by z_1 and z_2 that are related to two other variables, y_1 and y_2, by the linear equations

$$z_1 = a_{11}y_1 + a_{12}y_2$$

$$z_2 = a_{21}y_1 + a_{22}y_2$$

In matrix form, these equations would be written as

$$\begin{bmatrix} z_1 \\ z_2 \end{bmatrix} = \begin{bmatrix} a_{11} & a_{12} \\ a_{21} & a_{22} \end{bmatrix} \begin{bmatrix} y_1 \\ y_2 \end{bmatrix}$$

or more compactly as

$$z = \mathbf{A}y$$

in which z is the column vector with elements z_1 and z_2, $\mathbf{A}$ is the 2×2 matrix and y is the column vector with elements y_1 and y_2. The variables, y_1 and y_2, may be related to two other variables, x_1 and x_2, by the linear transformation

$$y_1 = b_{11}x_1 + b_{12}x_2$$

$$y_2 = b_{21}x_1 + b_{22}x_2$$

which would be written in matrix form as

$$\begin{bmatrix} y_1 \\ y_2 \end{bmatrix} = \begin{bmatrix} b_{11} & b_{12} \\ b_{21} & b_{22} \end{bmatrix} \begin{bmatrix} x_1 \\ x_2 \end{bmatrix}$$

or

$$y = \mathbf{B}x$$

The product matrix is formed by substituting $y = \mathbf{B}x$ into $z = \mathbf{A}y$ to give $z = \mathbf{AB}x$. The product matrix $\mathbf{AB}$ is seen to result from two successive transformations, one relates the variables z_1 and z_2 to y_1 and y_2 and the other which relates y_1 and y_2 to the variables x_1 and x_2.

Self test questions 7.4

The variables z_1 and z_2 are related to y_1 and y_2 by the equations

$$z_1 = y_1 + 3y_2 \quad \text{and} \quad z_2 = 2y_1 + y_2$$

If y_1 and y_2 are related to x_1 and x_2 by the equations

$$y_1 = 2x_1 - x_2 \quad \text{and} \quad y_2 = x_1 + 2x_2$$

write down the equations relating z_1 and z_2 to x_1 and x_2.

Unlike the multiplication of numbers and algebraic variables, matrix multiplication is not necessarily commutative. This means that a matrix product $\mathbf{AB}$ need not be the same as the product $\mathbf{BA}$. For example, the product

$$\begin{bmatrix} 1 & 1 \\ 2 & 1 \end{bmatrix} \begin{bmatrix} 2 & 2 \\ 1 & -1 \end{bmatrix} = \begin{bmatrix} 3 & 1 \\ 5 & 3 \end{bmatrix}$$

is not the same when the order of multiplication is reversed:

$$\begin{bmatrix} 2 & 2 \\ 1 & -1 \end{bmatrix} \begin{bmatrix} 1 & 1 \\ 2 & 1 \end{bmatrix} = \begin{bmatrix} 6 & 4 \\ -1 & 0 \end{bmatrix}$$

If the product $\mathbf{AB}$ is the same as the product $\mathbf{BA}$, the matrices $\mathbf{A}$ and $\mathbf{B}$ are said to **commute**.

Self test questions 7.5

Show that the following matrices $\mathbf{A}$ and $\mathbf{B}$ commute, that is $\mathbf{AB} = \mathbf{BA}$.

$$\mathbf{A} = \begin{bmatrix} 0 & 1 \\ 1 & 0 \end{bmatrix}, \quad \mathbf{B} = \begin{bmatrix} 2 & 3 \\ 3 & 2 \end{bmatrix}$$

7.4 **The unit matrix**

The **unit matrix** has 1's along the principal diagonal (the diagonal that runs from top left to bottom right) and 0's elsewhere. A 3×3 unit matrix is shown below:

$$\mathbf{I} = \begin{bmatrix} 1 & 0 & 0 \\ 0 & 1 & 0 \\ 0 & 0 & 1 \end{bmatrix}$$

The unit matrix has the property that it will **commute** with any other matrix of the same order and when it multiplies another matrix, the other matrix is unchanged. These properties are summarised by $\mathbf{AI} = \mathbf{IA} = \mathbf{A}$.

7.5 **The determinant of a matrix**

The determinant of the matrix is denoted by $|\mathbf{A}|$ and for a 2×2 matrix has the value shown below:

$$\mathbf{A} = \begin{bmatrix} a_{11} & a_{12} \\ a_{21} & a_{22} \end{bmatrix}, \qquad |\mathbf{A}| = \begin{vmatrix} a_{11} & a_{12} \\ a_{21} & a_{22} \end{vmatrix} = a_{11}a_{22} - a_{12}a_{21}$$

For example, if

$$\mathbf{A} = \begin{bmatrix} 1 & 2 \\ 2 & 1 \end{bmatrix} \qquad \text{then} \qquad |\mathbf{A}| = 1 - 4 = -3$$

If the determinant of a matrix is zero, it is said to be **singular** and is non-singular otherwise. For a matrix of order 3×3, the determinant can be evaluated as follows. If

$$\mathbf{A} = \begin{bmatrix} a_{11} & a_{12} & a_{13} \\ a_{21} & a_{22} & a_{23} \\ a_{31} & a_{32} & a_{33} \end{bmatrix}$$

then $|\mathbf{A}|$ can be written as

$$|\mathbf{A}| = a_{11} \begin{vmatrix} a_{22} & a_{23} \\ a_{32} & a_{33} \end{vmatrix} - a_{12} \begin{vmatrix} a_{21} & a_{23} \\ a_{31} & a_{33} \end{vmatrix} + a_{13} \begin{vmatrix} a_{21} & a_{22} \\ a_{31} & a_{32} \end{vmatrix}$$

Here, the determinant has been written down in terms of the elements of the top row of the matrix, a_{11}, a_{12} and a_{13}. The second order determinant that is multiplied by a_{11} is obtained by crossing out the row and column containing a_{11} and constructing the determinant from the elements that remain. The two other determinants are found in a similar way and the sign before the coefficients a_{11}, a_{12} and a_{13} alternates as shown. Although this expression for the third order determinant has been written out in terms of elements of the top row of the matrix, any row or column could be used. Determinants are used in finding reciprocal matrices and in the solution of sets of linear equations.

| 7.6 | **The inverse of a matrix** |

The inverse of a matrix is written as $\mathbf{A}^{-1}$. The inverse matrix has the property that $\mathbf{A}\mathbf{A}^{-1} = \mathbf{A}^{-1}\mathbf{A} = \mathbf{I}$, where $\mathbf{I}$ is the unit matrix. If variables y are related to variables x by the matrix equation $y = \mathbf{A}x$, then the variables that make up the column vector x are written in terms of those that make up the column vector y by the equation $x = \mathbf{A}^{-1}y$. Only matrices with non-singular determinants have an inverse and, in those cases, the method of finding the inverse follows well-defined steps that can be applied generally, but will not be gone through here. These steps entail evaluating the determinant of the matrix that is being inverted. For the 2×2 matrix

$$\mathbf{A} = \begin{bmatrix} a & b \\ c & d \end{bmatrix}$$

we have

$$\mathbf{A}^{-1} = \frac{1}{(ad - bc)} \begin{bmatrix} d & -b \\ -c & a \end{bmatrix}$$

It is clear from this that for the matrix $\mathbf{A}^{-1}$ to exist, the determinant $ad - bc$ must not be zero.

Self test questions 7.6

Determine the inverses of the matrices

(a) $\begin{bmatrix} 1 & 1 \\ 0 & 1 \end{bmatrix}$, (b) $\begin{bmatrix} 0 & 1 \\ 1 & 2 \end{bmatrix}$

| 7.7 | **Diagonal matrices** |

A **diagonal** matrix is one in which all the elements off the principal diagonal are zero. The form of such a matrix is

$$\begin{bmatrix} a_{11} & 0 & 0 \\ 0 & a_{22} & 0 \\ 0 & 0 & a_{33} \end{bmatrix}$$

The multiplication of diagonal matrices is commutative, that is $\mathbf{AB} = \mathbf{BA}$ if both $\mathbf{A}$ and $\mathbf{B}$ are diagonal. Matrices that are not diagonal can be transformed into diagonal form but, except for low order matrices, this is not usually a simple process in practice.

7.8 The transpose of a matrix

The transpose of the matrix $\mathbf{A}$ is obtained by interchanging the rows and columns of $\mathbf{A}$ and would be denoted by $\tilde{\mathbf{A}}$. For example, if $\mathbf{A}$ is the matrix

$$\mathbf{A} = \begin{bmatrix} 1 & 2 \\ 1 & 3 \end{bmatrix}$$

then

$$\tilde{\mathbf{A}} = \begin{bmatrix} 1 & 1 \\ 2 & 3 \end{bmatrix}$$

If we denote an element of $\mathbf{A}$ by a_{ij} then the corresponding element of $\tilde{\mathbf{A}}$ would be $\tilde{a}_{ij} = a_{ji}$.

7.9 Matrices as representations of symmetry operations

Matrices are a convenient way of representing operations such as rotation about an axis or reflection in a plane. In what follows, we will refer to **vectors** which for this purpose can be regarded as simply lines which have both a magnitude (length) and also a direction. A vector will be denoted in bold as in $\boldsymbol{u}$. Figure 7.1(a) shows a vector $\boldsymbol{u}$ that lies in the xy plane of the xyz coordinate system. The vector $\boldsymbol{u}$ can be specified by its x and y components u_x and u_y which are the projections of the tip of the vector on the x and y-axes. For a vector in the xy plane $u_z = 0$. The tip of the vector $\boldsymbol{u}$ would be said to have x, y, and z coordinates of $(u_x, u_y, 0)$ Figure 7.1(b) shows the diagram as it would appear looking down along the z-axis. Also shown is the vector $\boldsymbol{u}'$ that is obtained by rotating the vector $\boldsymbol{u}$ through an angle of $180°$ about the z-axis.

The vector $\boldsymbol{u}'$ has x, y and z coordinates of $(-u_x, -u_y, 0)$. The effect of the rotation through $180°$ on the vector $\boldsymbol{u}$ can be represented by the

Figure 7.1

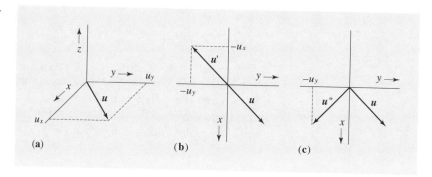

(a) (b) (c)

matrix equation

$$
\begin{bmatrix} u'_x \\ u'_y \\ u'_z \end{bmatrix} = \begin{bmatrix} -u_x \\ -u_y \\ 0 \end{bmatrix} = \begin{bmatrix} -1 & 0 & 0 \\ 0 & -1 & 0 \\ 0 & 0 & 1 \end{bmatrix} \begin{bmatrix} u_x \\ u_y \\ 0 \end{bmatrix}
$$

The 3×3 matrix shown represents the operation of rotation through $180°$ about the z-axis. Similarly, a reflection in the xz plane will give a vector u'' for which u''_y is equal to $-u_y$ as indicated in Figure 7.1(c) but the x and z components are unchanged:

$$
\begin{bmatrix} u''_x \\ u''_y \\ u''_z \end{bmatrix} = \begin{bmatrix} u_x \\ -u_y \\ u_z \end{bmatrix} = \begin{bmatrix} 1 & 0 & 0 \\ 0 & -1 & 0 \\ 0 & 0 & 1 \end{bmatrix} \begin{bmatrix} u_x \\ u_y \\ 0 \end{bmatrix}
$$

It is readily seen that reflection in the yz plane will have the effect of reversing the sign on the x-component of the vector, leaving the y and z components unchanged. This reflection would be represented by the matrix

$$
\begin{bmatrix} -1 & 0 & 0 \\ 0 & 1 & 0 \\ 0 & 0 & 1 \end{bmatrix}
$$

Answers **to self test questions**

7.1 $2x + y = p,\ x - y = q$

7.2 $\begin{bmatrix} 7 & 3 \\ -3 & 7 \end{bmatrix}$

7.3 (a) $\begin{bmatrix} 4 & 5 \\ 1 & 1 \end{bmatrix}$, (b) $\begin{bmatrix} -1 & -3 \\ 2 & -2 \end{bmatrix}$

7.4 $z_1 = 5x_1 + 5x_2, z_2 = 5x_1$

7.5 $\mathbf{AB} = \begin{bmatrix} 3 & 2 \\ 2 & 3 \end{bmatrix} = \mathbf{BA}$

7.6   (a) $\begin{bmatrix} 1 & -1 \\ 0 & 1 \end{bmatrix}$, (b) $\begin{bmatrix} -2 & 1 \\ 1 & 0 \end{bmatrix}$

Questions   **on Chapter 7**

7.1   From the two matrices

$$\mathbf{A} = \begin{bmatrix} 1 & 0 & 0 \\ 1 & 1 & 1 \\ 1 & 0 & 1 \end{bmatrix} \quad \text{and} \quad \mathbf{B} = \begin{bmatrix} 2 & 1 & 1 \\ 1 & 2 & 2 \\ 1 & 1 & 1 \end{bmatrix}$$

form the matrices $\mathbf{A} + \mathbf{B}$ and $3\mathbf{A} - \mathbf{B}$

7.2   Write down the three equations that express the variables p, q and r in terms of the variables x, y and z if

$$\begin{bmatrix} p \\ q \\ r \end{bmatrix} = \begin{bmatrix} 1 & 1 & 3 \\ 2 & 1 & 1 \\ 2 & 1 & 2 \end{bmatrix} \begin{bmatrix} x \\ y \\ z \end{bmatrix}$$

7.3   Given the two matrices

$$\mathbf{A} = \begin{bmatrix} 0 & 1 \\ 1 & 0 \end{bmatrix} \quad \text{and} \quad \mathbf{B} = \begin{bmatrix} 1 & 0 \\ 0 & -1 \end{bmatrix}$$

show that $\mathbf{AB} = -\mathbf{BA}$

7.4   Show that $\mathbf{AB} = \mathbf{O}$ where $\mathbf{O}$ is the zero matrix (all elements $= 0$) when

$$\mathbf{A} = \begin{bmatrix} 1 & 1 \\ 2 & 2 \end{bmatrix} \quad \text{and} \quad \mathbf{B} = \begin{bmatrix} -1 & 1 \\ 1 & -1 \end{bmatrix}$$

7.5   Find the matrix product $\mathbf{AB}$ when

$$\mathbf{A} = \begin{bmatrix} 2 & 1 & 0 \\ 1 & 1 & 2 \\ 2 & 1 & 0 \end{bmatrix} \quad \text{and} \quad \mathbf{B} = \begin{bmatrix} 1 & 2 & 1 \\ 1 & 1 & 1 \\ 2 & 2 & 1 \end{bmatrix}$$

7.6   Find the product $\mathbf{A}^{-1}\mathbf{B}^{-1}$ when

$$\mathbf{A} = \begin{bmatrix} 1 & 1 \\ 1 & 2 \end{bmatrix} \quad \text{and} \quad \mathbf{B} = \begin{bmatrix} 1 & 0 \\ 1 & 1 \end{bmatrix}$$

7.7 Write the equations

$$x - y = 2$$

$$2x + y = 1$$

in the matrix form $\mathbf{A}x = c$ where

$$x = \begin{bmatrix} x \\ y \end{bmatrix} \quad \text{and} \quad c = \begin{bmatrix} 2 \\ 1 \end{bmatrix}$$

Determine the inverse matrix $\mathbf{A}^{-1}$ and hence find the values of x and y from $x = \mathbf{A}^{-1}c$.

7.8 Show that the determinant of the matrix $\mathbf{A}$ is equal to 5 when

$$\mathbf{A} = \begin{bmatrix} 1 & 4 & 2 \\ 3 & -2 & 1 \\ 1 & 5 & 2 \end{bmatrix}$$

7.9 Show that the transpose of the product $\mathbf{AB}$ is equal to $\tilde{\mathbf{B}}\tilde{\mathbf{A}}$ using the matrices

$$\mathbf{A} = \begin{bmatrix} 1 & 3 \\ 2 & 4 \end{bmatrix} \quad \text{and} \quad \mathbf{B} = \begin{bmatrix} 2 & -1 \\ 3 & 1 \end{bmatrix}$$

7.10 A rotation through the angle θ about the z-axis of the xyz coordinate system can be represented by the matrix

$$\mathbf{R} = \begin{bmatrix} \cos\theta & \sin\theta & 0 \\ \sin\theta & \cos\theta & 0 \\ 0 & 0 & 1 \end{bmatrix}$$

Write down the matrix that represents a rotation through $120°$. (Note that $\cos 60° = 1/2$ and $\sin 60° = \sqrt{3}/2$.)

Index